WOLVERCOTE MILL

The Paper Mill at Wolvercote, Oxfordshire, belonging to James Swan, Esq.

The Paper Mill at Wolvercote, Oxfordshire, belonging to James Swan, Esq.' A water-colour drawing, signed
... by ... ... From the original, size 15 in. by 10 in, in the possession of the Printer to the

WOLVERCOTE MILL

A Study in Paper-Making at Oxford

BY

HARRY CARTER

OXFORD

AT THE CLARENDON PRESS

1957

Oxford University Press, Amen House, London E.C.4

GLASGOW NEW YORK TORONTO MELBOURNE WELLINGTON
BOMBAY CALCUTTA MADRAS KARACHI KUALA LUMPUR
CAPE TOWN IBADAN NAIROBI ACCRA

PREFACE

by the Controller of the Mill

WOLVERCOTE Mill has been associated with printing at Oxford for nearly three centuries and for the last of the three it has been owned and managed by the University. In recent years early English paper-mills and their records have attracted the attention of scholars, and since it seemed likely that the records of the mill, at Wolvercote and in the Press archives, would make a contribution not only to the history of paper-making but, in a small way, to that of the University and to book-production in Oxford, I invited, with the encouragement of the Delegates of the Press, Mr. Harry Carter, the Printer's archivist, to investigate the history of the mill.

The mill has always found the main outlet for its products in Oxford. In early days its proximity to one of the three places in England where printing was allowed favoured the manufacture of white paper, and in more recent times it is probably to its connexion with the University that it owes its survival. Wolvercote paper was used at Dr. Fell's press in the Sheldonian Theatre and thus survives in some of the early books printed for the University. While still in private hands, the mill supplied much of the paper for the Bible and the Learned Presses and today supplies an ever-increasing amount of the paper used by the publishing departments of the Press.

It is hoped that students of paper-making further afield may find some value in this record. Mr. Carter's researches have shown that the mill, with its early conversion to paper-making, was a pioneer in a number of changes that illustrate the development of the industry away from the main centres of production. Some of the Wolvercote millers—Quelch, Beckford, and Swann—deserve to be remembered as men who have left their mark on the history of their trade.

[v]

Today the mill is one of two survivors of what was once a numerous group of mills on the upper Thames, whose influence on the economics of the region was considerable; those at Eynsham, Sandford, and Hampton Gay had links with Wolvercote and with the Press at Oxford. The mill and its activities have also been a dominant theme in the history of the village, which still has to be written. We have thought its local interest, particularly to those who work there, a sufficient excuse for tracing the water-mill in medieval records and for adding notes on the surrounding fields and landmarks, from the deeds preserved by the University and the Press.

This year provides an appropriate occasion for a history of the mill. The volume appears 100 years after the first delivery of paper made by the University and, so far as can be told, 300 years after the beginning of paper-making on this site. It comes, also, at the end of an epoch; for the decision of the Delegates of the Press in 1954 to rebuild and enlarge their mill has altered the whole character of paper-making at Wolvercote. From this standpoint, we can look back with detachment on the past 300 years and on a type of mill that will soon be forgotten except in so far as history can preserve it.

J. RODERICK HENDERSON

Wolvercote Paper Mill
Oxford
May 1957

ACKNOWLEDGEMENTS

I HAVE to thank His Grace the Duke of Marlborough for permission to read and quote documents at Blenheim Estate Office and Mr. W. L. Murdock for producing them. I owe some of the information in the book to Mr. Peter Walne, Berkshire County Archivist; Mr. H. M. Walton, of Oxfordshire County Record Office; Dr. D. C. Coleman, of the London School of Economics; Mr. R. H. Clapperton; Professor Herbert Davis; Dr. F. V. Price; and Mr. L. W. Hanson. Dr. A. H. Shorter, of Exeter University, and Mrs. Susan Wood, of St. Hugh's College, Oxford, were kind enough to give me the benefit of their expert knowledge, one of the history of English paper-mills, and the other of the history of the region.

H. C.

CONTENTS

List of Illustrations   *page* xi

I. The Mill and the River   1

II. The Early History of the Mill   10

III. The Era of Hand-made Paper and the First Machine   18

IV. Thomas Combe at the Mill House   32

V. The Mill under the Partners   39

VI. Recent History   49

VII. Topographical Notes on the Site   59

Appendixes

     I. A Memorandum of 1696 on the failure of the Company of White Paper Makers   66

     II. Inventory of Stock for Paper-making at the Mill, 1782   67

     III. Proposals by the Bible Committee of the Delegates of the Press for the acquisition of Wolvercote Mill, 1855   68

     IV. Paper-mills near Oxford in 1816   70

     V. Notes on Drawback of Duties on Paper allowed to the Universities   71

Index   73

LIST OF ILLUSTRATIONS

Water-colour drawing of the mill by John Buckler, 1826   *frontispiece*

Part of Andrews's and Dury's *Map of the Country Round London*, 1 in. to the mile, 1777   *page 2*

Plan of the site and surroundings of Wolvercote Mill based on one in the Particulars of Sale of the Duke of Marlborough's lands in Lower Wolvercote, 1884   *page 5*

The mill-stream   *facing p. 6*

King's Weir and the Weir-keeper's cottage (about 1865)

Workmen's cottages and Church School at Lower Wolvercote built by Thomas Combe   *facing p. 7*

Watermarks of T. Q. (Thomas Quelch), 1685   *page 19*

Watermark of J. S. (John Swann), 1794   *page 25*

Watermarks of I. S. (John Swann), 1798   *page 26*

The Mill House from the garden (before 1883). *Photograph by J. H. Stacy*   *facing p. 32*

Portrait of Thomas Combe by J. E. Millais, 1850. *Ashmolean Museum, Oxford*   *facing p. 33*

Mrs. Combe by J. E. Millais (1849). *Ashmolean Museum, Oxford*   *page 38*

J. H. Stacy in a group. A photograph of about 1865   *facing p. 48*

Photograph of Thomas Combe, Professor Bartholomew Price, and others at the Mill House. *Photograph by J. H. Stacy, 1871*   *facing p. 49*

Plans of the mill, 1849, 1864, 1872, and 1917   *page 52*

The mill built in 1855–6. *Photograph by J. H. Stacy*   *facing p. 54*

J. Castle and his staff making hay, about 1890   *facing p. 55*

Air photograph of the mill and site, 1950   *facing p. 58*

The Weighbridge House, once the 'Crown' ale-house   *facing p. 59*

[xi]

The initial letters to the chapters are some that were engraved for Dr. Fell, Dean of Christ Church, about 1674 by George Edwardes, who is reputed to have begun the making of book-papers at Wolvercote. See p. 14.

I · THE MILL AND THE RIVER

WOLVERCOTE Mill gave up using water-power in 1943. For nearly three centuries before that time water-wheels, first one, then two, and for a time three, worked an engine for breaking and beating pulp and rags. The mill-wheels were taken out in 1950, and no rags have been used at Wolvercote since 1952.

Now the river does no more than supply the water used in paper-making,[1] at present 10,000 gallons an hour, and carry it away again after use. The river is still vital to the paper-making business; but its rapid fall after rounding the hills at Godstow is now only an historical reason for the siting of the mill.

For six centuries, certainly, and probably much longer, the fall of 4 feet 6 inches in winter and 3 feet 3 inches in summer, contrived by the management of an arm of the Thames two miles above Oxford and some smaller streams feeding it, was made to work a mill. Flour, cloth, swords, and paper are known to have been produced with the aid of the power of the fall.

Just over a hundred million gallons of water passed under the mill during twenty-four hours in January 1885 at a speed of 1 foot a second. Falling 4 feet, this water represents about 60 horse power, of which 80 per cent. could be turned to industrial account by a water-wheel. In a dry summer it was reckoned that the volume of water was rather less than half the maximum, and the average power all the year round was considered to be worth in 1885, £50 for the year.[2]

[1] A typical chemical analysis of the Thames water here is: hardness 300 p.p.m.; pH 7·5; B.O.D. 7 p.p.m.; suspended solids 13 p.p.m.

[2] The figures in this paragraph were provided by the Controller, Joseph Castle, in 1885 as a basis for reckoning the rateable value of the mill (Envelope No. 419, M).

In the footnotes custody of documents is shown by the abbreviations M for Mill, CP for Clarendon Press, P for Printer to the University.

The arm of the Thames that worked the mill has in winter an average width of 42 feet and a depth of 4 feet 6 inches. The difference between winter and summer levels is about 1 foot 3 inches. The main stream of the river in these parts has about three times this volume of water; and the flow to Wolvercote Mill, winter and summer, depends almost entirely on the level of the Thames where it feeds the mill-stream above Wolvercote and the speed of the stream there. These are regulated by a weir across the main stream known for many centuries past as King's Weir. Seasonal and casual variations in the water diverted from the main river to the mill were adjusted to the capacity of the mill-race in the way customary among millers, by dividing the mill-stream above the mill into mill-head and backwater, so that more or less of it could be wasted. There was a difference of 7 inches between the top of the weir and the sill of the mill-race.[1]

There were times in dry seasons when the water-mill could not work when King's Weir let any water pass over it; and then the reach of the river below became almost dry.[2] And on one occasion at least the maintenance of a high level in the mill-stream caused flooding of the meadows and streets of Yarnton.[3] The give and take between miller and other riparian dwellers and owners of water-rights gave rise to constant disputes and a complicated system of law and custom. The mill was often at a standstill for lack of water and occasionally because of abnormal floods.[4]

It is not surprising that from very early times the ownership of King's Weir went with the property in the mill, or that the management of the weir had to reconcile conflicting interests.

[1] Joseph Castle's Pocket-book, p. 98, 4 Oct. 1885 (M).
[2] Paper headed 'King's Weir' in J. H. Stacy's handwriting, undated (M).
[3] B. Stapleton, *Three Oxfordshire Parishes*, Oxf. Hist. Soc., xxiv. 280, 316.
[4] Letter from James Swann, of Eynsham, to James Blackstone, 7 Sept. 1808, Blenheim Estate Office.

On the opposite page is a reproduction of part of Andrews's and Dury's *Map of the Country Round London*, 1 in. to the mile, 1777 (slightly reduced).

The oldest record of King's Weir, made in 1189,[1] describes it as used for trapping fish, and in early times there were people in Wolvercote and Oxford, no doubt also in the adjoining riverside villages, who made a living as fishermen. Another powerful interest came into being in 1636 when the Thames was made navigable as far as Oxford,[2] at a time when the level of water in the reach of the river past the city depended on King's Weir. In 1751 an act was passed and commissioners were appointed to regulate the state of the locks and weirs from Oxford to Cricklade.[3] In the nineteenth century barges went up to the weir, and under the powers given them by Thames Navigation Act of 1865 the Thames Conservators required the owner of King's Weir to open the sluice-gates to let boats pass and, twice a week for a spell of three hours, to fill the lower reach.[4] During the three-hour 'flashes' work at the mill stopped for lack of water. About 1860 the river was allowed to silt up between Oxford and Wolvercote, and navigation went by way of the canal back into an arm of the river at Duke's Lock near Yarnton. By arrangement with the boatmen the Manager of the mill stopped the flashes so that the mill worked continuously. But not long before 1872 Mr. Campbell, of Buscot Park, and others prevailed with the Thames Conservancy to restore the navigation of this part of the river; the Conservancy rebuilt the locks at Medley and Godstow and widened and repaired King's Weir.[5] Thereafter the owners of the mill periodically agitated for the build-

[1] 'Una piscaria quae vocatur Kiniseswerc', c. 1404 (Charter of 1 Ric. I): Dugd. Monasticon, iv. 364; 'A fysshynge were wt wereham', c. 1450: English Leiger Book of Godstow, Bodl. MS. Rawl. B. 480, fol IIv; 'one ffyssh were that is called the kyngis were', ibid., fol. 186v.

[2] Laud's Remains: Second Volume, ed. H. Wharton, 1700, p. 81. See T. S. Willan, 'Navigation of the Thames and Kennett', Berks. Arch. J. xl (1936), 146, and I. G. Philip, 'River Navigation at Oxford during the Civil War, etc.', Oxoniensia, II (1939), p. 152.

[3] An Act for the better carrying on and regulating the navigation of the rivers Thames and Isis, etc., 24 Geo. II, c. 6.

[4] Letter, J. H. Stacy to Prof. B. Price, 8 Nov. 1872 (M). The power to require the opening of weirs had previously been given to Justices of the Peace by an Act of 6–7 William & Mary (c. 16).

[5] Ibid.

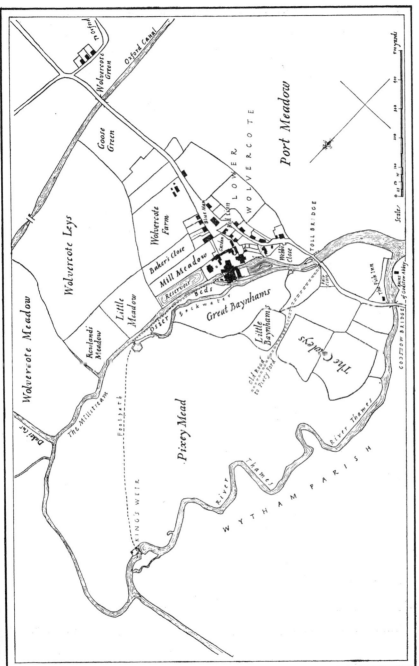

Plan of the site and surroundings of Wolvercote Mill based on one in the Particulars of Sale of the Duke of Marlborough's lands in Lower Wolvercote, 1884.

ing of a lock to save the opening of the weir whenever boats passed.[1] The question of building a pound-lock there was considered by the Duke of Marlborough as early as 1782;[2] the Thames Navigation Commissioners resolved in 1818 to build one 'as soon as sufficient money can be raised'; but there the matter rested until 1928, when the present King's Weir Lock was at last made.[3] In 1885 the weir was acquired by the Thames Valley Drainage Board and thoroughly repaired.[4] The millowners were jealous of any fresh calls on the river-water; and in 1865 they entered their objections to the Cheltenham and Gloucester Waterworks Bill because it proposed to divert water from the Thames by sinking a well at South Cerney, in Gloucestershire.[5]

So long as the mill produced only hand-made papers, waterpower to drive the engines for breaking and pulping the rags was enough motive force: but when a machine for making paper was bought in 1811 and a coal-fed steam-engine was installed to drive it, the river took on a new function as a medium for transporting the coal. The University's Delegates, the lessees of the mill, bought two barges in 1856, which plied by turns between Wolvercote and collieries in the Midlands, until, refusing to meet the demands for higher wages from the bargees, the Delegates sold them in 1916. But coal was brought to the mill by water until 1950.[6]

In 1884 coal was thus brought from Moira Colliery in

[1] Letters and papers at the mill show that the University negotiated with the Thames Conservancy on this subject in 1873 and 1885; but the T.C. wanted the mill to bear the whole cost.
[2] Estimate by J. Simcock, 1782, at Blenheim Estate Office.
[3] Minutes of the Thames Nav. Commissioners, 27 Dec. 1817 and 17 Jan. 1818; Berks. County Record Office.
[4] Papers and plans relating to the compulsory acquisition of the weir by the Thames Valley Drainage Commissioners are at the mill. The price paid was £5.
[5] Draft petition by Combe, Hall, and Latham to the House of Commons, dated 18 Feb. 1865 (M).
[6] Joseph Castle's Pocket-book (M); recollections of Mr. E. E. Collett.

The illustration on the opposite page shows the mill-stream just above the mill.

King's Weir, photographed about 1865

The street of Lower Wolvercote about 1875. The cottages and school-room were
built by Thomas Combe. *Photographs by J. H. Stacy*

Leicestershire to the wharf behind the mill at a cost of 13s. 4d. a ton, the price delivered by rail and cart being 4d. more. By 1897 the price had risen to 14s. 4½d., and by 1916 it was 19s. 8¾d. by canal-boat and 19s. 11d. by rail. By that time consumption of coal at the mill was roughly 100 tons a week.[1]

It was the cost of coal that drove paper-makers away from the upper Thames, where there were many at one time.[2] A small mill at Wolvercote could not have made paper by machinery in the days of steam unless it had some protection against competition from mills nearer the coalfields or the sea. It was saved by its connexion with the University Press, until the National Grid supplying electric power freed it from entire dependence on coal supplied to the door. Coal-fired boilers are still used to dry the paper and heat the building.

For many years the bugbear of expensive coal hindered development of the mill. From 1855 to 1898 it worked with one machine; and when a second was finally installed it was in face of grave misgivings on the part of the Secretary of the University's Delegates for the Press. 'I should strongly dissuade the expenditure of £10,000', he wrote, 'if it were going to be sunk (as similar sums have been sunk in the decaying paper-mills of the upper Thames) with the certainty that the new machinery would cost twice as much in coal to keep going as the machinery of the competing mills in other parts of England.'[3] In 1872 the ruinous price of coal (about 12s. a ton) and, indeed the impossibility, it was said, of getting it at all, made the Mill Manager, clinging to the use of water-power, propose the purchase of one of these decayed paper-mills, at Hampton Gay, as an accessory plant for breaking-in rags.[4]

The question of buying Cassington Mill, then lately fitted up as a flour-mill, was also mooted in 1872;[5] but neither it nor

---

1 The figures are taken from Castle's Pocket-book.
2 See Appendix IV.
3 Lyttelton-Gell to Castle, 9 Oct. 1897 (M).
4 Letter from J. H. Stacy to Prof. B. Price, 10 July 1872 (M).
5 Ibid.

Hampton Gay was bought. But mills on the upper river were offered at reasonable prices, and in 1880, mainly to gain control of the water-level at Oxford, the University's Delegates of the Press bought the large paper-mill at Sandford, below Oxford, where wrapping-papers and board were produced.[1] After a brief spell of management by the Delegates and the installation of a water-turbine and new paper-making machinery, Sandford Mill was let in 1882 and sold to the tenants in 1918.[2] The purchase of Weirs Mill, in Oxford, where wallpaper was made about that time, was considered in 1882.[3] The oldest workers at Wolvercote Mill can remember no other paper-mills in the region but these and the mill at Eynsham, where the manufacture of paper stopped not long before 1900.[4]

Of the links between paper-making and rivers, by no means the least important is the need for a channel to carry off the effluent. In 1869 the mill was using 254,000 gallons of the river-water a day, and returning it to the river in a more or less polluted state, where it mixed with 1,400 times its volume in winter and half that amount in summer.[5] The matter introduced into this water at the mill and turned into the river was vividly described by the Manager at about the same time (1866–70):[6]

The materials which have been found most advantageous in making paper for the Oxford Press are canvas sails and cotton rags in about equal proportions. The principal impurities in the former are the tarred thread with which the sails are sewn and particles of pitch from the ships' decks and rigging. The bulk of the cotton rags are generally of a lower character, and (in addition to wool and silk woven with the fabric) contain a perceptible quantity of animal matter, the nature of which may be imagined, when

[1] *V.C.H. Oxon.* ii. 240; Delegates' Orders, 1881–92, p. 30 (CP).
[2] Ibid.; Finance File 'Outside businesses: Sandford Paper Mill' (CP).
[3] Delegates' Orders, 1881–92, p. 60 (CP).
[4] Swann & Blake occur in the Wolvercote accounts for the last time in 1861 (P). Eynsham Paper Mills Co. Ltd. (in liquidation) appears in the *Directory of Paper Makers, 1894.*
[5] Draft letter from J. H. Stacy to the Thames Conservators, 9 Aug. 1869 (M).
[6] Undated letter from J. H. Stacy to B. Price (M).

it is stated that they are the cast-off garments of the lowest class of society. . . . The animal matter is very perceptible to the smell.

The effluent was described in 1876 as '250,000 gallons of washing water and 4,000 gallons of black liquor'.[1] Settling-ponds for removing the worst from the black liquor were built in 1867;[2] but they did not satisfy the Thames Conservancy;[3] and in despair, it would seem, the Manager suggested that the offensive liquor should be exhausted as a fine spray down the mill chimney, whence it would pass as dry matter into the atmosphere.[4] Under the pressure of threats and remonstrances from the Conservancy, improvements were made in the settling-ponds from time to time. In 1904 a prosecution was begun, but withdrawn on condition that improvements in the disposal of the effluent were made reasonably soon. The volume of the effluent was then 130,000 gallons a day, equivalent, said the expert employed by the University, to the sewage from a town of 6,000 inhabitants, and an eighth of the objectionable matter produced by the mill passed into the river.[5] As rags were super-seded by wood-pulp, the problem of the effluent ceased to inflate the Controller's letter-files; but Henry Frowde, the Publisher to the University, wrote in 1917 that he remembered a time when it was feared that the mill would have to close because no solution to the problem could be found.[6]

[1] Memorandum by J. H. Stacy, 10 July 1876 (M).
[2] Ibid.
[3] In July 1876 the Thames Conservators notified the Mill Manager that they intended to enforce the Pollution of Rivers Act of that year upon him (M). It was the first of many such communications from them.
[4] Memo. by J. H. Stacy, 6 July 1876 (M).
[5] Letters and papers in an envelope marked 'Letters connected with the Effluent Business, 1904' (M).
[6] Letter to Charles Cannan, 16 Dec. 1917 in the file of 'Outside businesses: Sandford Mill' (CP).

II · THE EARLY HISTORY OF THE MILL

HE mill at Wolvercote was part of the endowment of Godstow nunnery, a Benedictine abbey dissolved in 1540, whose ruins lie about a mile to the west of the mill. At the time of the dissolution the water-mill and a fishery called the Kyng's Were were let to Hugh Weller at an annual rent of £6.[1]

The two register-books of the abbey, of which the older is believed to have been written in 1404,[2] give what purport to be copies of the documents granting the mill to the nuns. One of these, recording the dedication of the convent church in the reign of King Stephen, recites the gift to the foundation by John de St. John of a mill worth £4 (a year) in Wlgaricote and the dwellings of two men with their appurtenances and a parcel of land before the gateway of the church in the island which lies between two waters and half a meadow called Lambei. Robert de Ollei gave the other half of the same meadow, that is to say, Lambei, and a bushel of flour every year. The dedication can be roughly dated 1138.[3]

Another deed quoted in the register recites a gift by Bernard de St. Waleric (or St. Valery) to King Henry II of Wlgaricot and its subsequent grant by the king to the nuns of Godstow.[4] King Richard I confirmed the charters endowing Godstow, among them a gift by Reginald de St. Waleric of the mill of Wolgaricote and a fishery called Kiniseswere and meadows called Heringesham, Boieham and Licheseie and land which lies between two waters and half a meadow called Lambeie and a gift by Robert de Ollei of the other half of the same meadow.[5]

---

1 Dugd. *Mon.* iv. 370.
2 The dating of the manuscript authorities for the history of Godstow Abbey is discussed by A. Clark, *Wood's Life and Times*, iv, 1895 (Oxf. Hist. Soc., xxx), 96–97.   3 Dugd. *Mon.* iv. 362,
4 Ibid., p. 364.   5 Ibid.

There is a long lapse of time between the alleged gifts and the surviving records; but there is no good reason for doubting the general truth of the story implicit in the deeds. At the time of Domesday Roger de Ivry held land, meadows, and a fishery at Walton in the suburbs of Oxford, and his brother, Godfrey, held five hides of Roger in Ulfgarcote. The last d'Ivry died about 1112, and the king bestowed his honours on Guy de St. Walery.[1] About 1141 the Empress Maud deprived Reginald de St. Walery of his lands and gave them to her adherent John St. John.[2] In time of peace the lands were restored to St. Walery (about 1153).[3] It is probable enough, therefore, that both Reginald de St. Walery and John St. John, as conflicting claimants to the same land, granted the mill, whichever came second confirming the gift by the other, while, later, the whole manor that had belonged to St. Walery was given to the abbey by the king. As for Robert d'Oilly, he was descended from that Robert de Oilgi(e) who is recorded in Domesday as holding a fee partly inside and partly outside the wall of Oxford, including houses and 30 acres of meadow next to the wall and a mill; and these he held as one manor with the advowson of St. Peter.

In the Middle Ages Wolvercote was in the parish of St. Peter's in the East, Oxford, and its own place of worship was rated as a chapel of ease. Tithes due to the chapel were assigned to the vicar of the mother-church by the Bishop of Lincoln in 1237;[4] but his claim to them was disputed by Godstow Abbey. The vicar prosecuted his case by an appeal to Rome, and after a trial by an ecclesiastical court the tithes of the Abbey's property in Wolvercote were apportioned between Godstow Church and St. Peter's so that those due for the meadows, the mills (of which there seem to have been more than one), and the Abbey-servants (if the servants slept in Wolvercote, were not wives, and had no houses of their own) went to Godstow, while

---

[1] White Kennett, *Hist. of Ambrosden etc.*, 1695, p. 83.
[2] Ibid., p. 97.   [3] *V.C.H. Oxon.* i. 439.
[4] *Rotuli Roberti Grosseteste*, 1235–53, ed. F. N. Davies, London, Canterbury & York Soc., 1913, p. 450.

those arising from profits of villeinage and a meadow named Northmede went to St. Peter's; but two hams within Hertheshamme in Northmede, which never paid tithe, were excepted from the award and so were two acres in the same meadow which went with the mills and with them the dams of Mulecrophte.[1] The last clause may be taken to mean that there were reservoirs for flood-water in the paddock behind the mills, known as Mill Croft, and on much the same site as the existing reservoirs. The exceptions perhaps account for the extra-parochial character of part of the mill-site in modern times.[2] When the church of St. Peter's in the East was repaired in 1413, the people of Wolvercote had to pay a share of the cost;[3] and it was in the following year that the Pope allowed the church at Wolvercote to be consecrated and used for burials.[4] By the end of the sixteenth century the obligation of Wolvercote to the old mother-church had been commuted to a rent of £1 a year.[5]

One of the meadows named in the Godstow Abbey charters still forms part of the mill property: Boieham is now Baynhams. Little Lambheye is mentioned in the reigns of Henry VIII and James I.[6]

The earliest description of the mill property is in a survey of the domains of Godstow Abbey at the time of the Dissolution, in 1541 (in Latin except for the words in italics):

All that water-mill in Wolgercot called Wolgercot Mill, with all the waters, fisheries, meadows, *holtes*, *hinetes* and pieces of land appertaining, and one *le weyre* called *lekynges were* with all several waters and fisheries and their appurtenances with one cottage and six acres of arable-and-pasture land lying in Wolvercote in the fields there.[7]

Medieval documents make no mention of the use to which

[1] B.M. Add. Ch. 10639.   [2] See p. 30 and the 6-in. Ordnance Map.
[3] *Hearne's Collections*, ed. C. E. Doble, vol. ii, 1889 (Oxf. Hist. Soc. xiii), 74. See also vol. i, 196.
[4] *Calendar of Papal Registers: Papal Letters*, Public Record Office, vol. vi, p. 441.   [5] Churchwardens' Accounts of St. Peter's in the East.
[6] Dugd. *Mon.* iv. 376; Cal. Inq. P.M., Ser. II, 304, No. 47. Possibly 'Lichesei' (1138) was a mis-spelled early form of Pixey Mead.
[7] P.R.O., Exch. Augm., Partic. for Grants, Hen. 8, Owen (1).

the mill was put; but the presumption that it ground corn as part of a village economy is supported by the name of the tenant at the time of the dissolution of the abbey; for people of the name of Weller were yeomen-farmers of Lower Wolvercote for many generations afterwards.[1] Names of later landlords are known: from the abbey the mill passed to Sir George Owen, physician to Henry VIII, whose descendants sold it in 1616 to Sir John Walter of Sarsden,[2] in whose family it remained until it was bought by the first Duke of Marlborough. At the time of the sale in 1616 there were two corn-mills, known as Wolvercote Milles, and a fulling-mill adjoining them.[3] But of millers no trace has been found until, in the middle of the seventeenth century, there is reason to think that King Charles I's armourers adapted one of the mills for grinding sword-blades whilst his headquarters were at Oxford. That this was so appears from the king's order on the Exchequer for an imprest of £100 to the Master of the Armoury 'to be imployed according as wee shall direct in the building of a Mill at Wolvercott near unto our Cittie of Oxford for grinding of swords, and for building of Forges, providing of Tooles and other necessaries for sword-blade Makers'.[4] Whether the intention was carried out and, if so, whether the sword-mill lasted longer than the two more years that the king spent at Oxford, there is no means of telling.

Nothing more is known of the mill until, in 1674, the learned Keeper of the Ashmolean Museum, Robert Plot, passed through Wolvercote and noted in his journal: 'they make a coarse paper at a mill here'.[5] But about this time it is known that paper made at Wolvercote began to be used by the press established by Oxford University in the new Sheldonian Theatre. A year or two after leasing this press in 1671, Dr. John Fell, Dean of

[1] P.R.O., Chanc. Proc. Series II, Bundle 326, 104 (1619); mortgage of 1621 in the Mill title-deeds (CP).

[2] P.R.O., L.T.R. Mem. Rolls, 13 Jas. I, Hil, m. 200 and 14 Jas. I, Mich., m. 166.   [3] Ibid., 13 Jas. I, Hil, m. 200.

[4] P.R.O., S.P. (Dom), Chas. I, 498, No. 8, p. 13. This was a discovery of the late Mr. Falconer Madan.

[5] Quoted from Hearne's transcript in Bodl. MS. Hearne's Diaries 158, p. 15.

Christ Church, on behalf of himself and his three partners in the lease, writes: 'We have paper made within two miles of this town that is usefull in printing.'[1] His statement and Plot's are not necessarily contradictory: Fell may have meant that the paper made at Wolvercote could be used for covers or even wrapping. He and his chief helper in conducting the learned press, Dr. Thomas Yate, bought most, if not all, of the printing paper used in their earlier years from Holland and France through London stationers.[2]

However, John Bagford, a London shoemaker and a great collector of information about printing, wrote in the year 1714 a rough draft for a history of printing at Oxford, in which, referring to Fell, he said: 'He likewise incouraged the fitting up of a Paper Mill at Wolvercut by Mr. George Edwards, who was a cutter of the great Letters, & Engraved many other things made use of in printing of Books, & had a Talent in Maps, altho' done with his left hand.'[3] A friend of Bagford's, on whom he seems to have relied for information, John Bullord, book-seller of St. Paul's Churchyard, left some rough notes for a history of paper, in which he wrote: 'The Mill at Wovellcut bult 1686 by Mr. Gorge Edwardes.'[4]

George Edwardes is known as an Oxford artist: he was em-ployed by Fell as an engraver in wood and copper in 1674–5;[5] he signed an undated receipt for £24 paid him by Fell for an alphabet of decorated letters cut in wood first used in 1674 (most of which still exist at the University Press);[6] and he

---

[1] All Souls College, MS. 239, fo. 667.
[2] Bodl. MS. Rawl. D. 398, fos. 156–7. See R. W. Chapman, 'An Inventory of Paper, 1674', *The Library*, 4 Ser. vii (1926), 402–8.
[3] B.M. Harl. MS. 5901, at fo. 86.
[4] Bodl. MS. Rawl. D. 398, fo. 4. These are apparently transcripts by Bagford of notes by John Bullord, book-auctioneer of London.
[5] According to F. Madan, *Oxford Books*, iii. 291, 329, Edwardes published his copper-engraved plates of academic costume in 1674 and did engraving in copper and wood for the Sheldonian Press in 1676 and 1677. Fell paid him £6 for the *Oxford Almanack* in 1675 and £2 for cuts in Scheffer's *History of Lapland*, 1674 (Univ. Archives, Chancellor's Court Cause-papers, Hilary 1687/88). See the note on p. xii.   [6] Bodl. MS. Rawl. D. 398, fo. 120b.

engraved for Oxford printers in 1676 and 1677. His name has not been found in records relating to Wolvercote.

A passage in one of Fell's letters to his partner, Sir Leoline Jenkins, suggests that the making at Wolvercote of paper suitable for books began not long before the time of writing: 29 October 1683.[1] 'I have this Morning sent you . . . a Specimen of our Oxford Paper for the ordinary Sort, which I hope by the next year to get emproved', he wrote, meaning presumably by 'the ordinary sort' printing of medium quality, and leaving it to be understood that imported paper would still be used for the more elaborate books.

Dr. Fell died in 1686. It was a significant year in the history of English paper-making because it followed the Revocation of the Edict of Nantes and the arrival of many Huguenot refugees in this country. Much of the book-paper used in England in the preceding years had been made around Angoulême in France by Protestant workmen in mills rented by Dutch or English stationers from Jesuit landlords.[2] With the end of toleration the stationers withdrew to their own countries and their workmen generally followed them. The Synod of Walloon Churches in Holland issued this instruction in 1688: 'Churches are notified, for the sake of avoiding liabilities, that when paper-makers' workmen apply to their deacons, they should be directed to England, to Mr. Paul Duppin in London, whose address they will easily learn from any of the Elders of the Walloon Churches of London. Mr. Duppin promises to find work for whole families, suitable to the capacity of each person.'[3] The Company of the White Paper Makers in England was incorporated by Royal Letters Patent in 1686.[4] The Company had a monopoly of making white paper (i.e. paper costing

[1] P.R.O., State Papers (Dom.) Chas. II, 434, No. 205.
[2] Auguste Lacroix, *Historique de la papeterie d'Angoulême*, Angoulême, 1853, pp. 8, 9.
[3] J. W. Enschedé, 'Papier en Papierhandel in Noord-Nederland, gedurende de xviie Eeuw', *Tijdschrift voor Boek- en Biblioteekwezen*, vii (1909), at p. 187.
[4] *Hist. MSS. Comm., 12th Report, App. Pt. 6, House of Lords MSS., 1689–90*, p. 299. The original is in the Patent Roll, 2 Jas. II, part 10, No. 17.

more than 4s. a ream) for the next fourteen years; a monopoly that appears not to have been enforced against the miller at Wolvercote.[1]

The evidence so far discovered for the beginning of paper-making at Wolvercote is far from clear or conclusive; but if it suggests that coarse paper was made there for a number of years before 1680 and fine paper soon thereafter, it accords with what is more reliably known about other paper-mills in England. And the later history of Wolvercote Mill (see p. 23) shows that when millers began to make paper, they did not always cease to grind corn: they carried on both businesses in one mill.

The state of this manufacture about 1690 is described in a pamphlet headed *The Case of the English Paper-Makers*:[2]

> The Ancient Manufacture of *English* Paper was only Brown-Paper and Coarse White, but of late years by great Charge and Industry it hath been improv'd to the making of such Paper as hath served both for Writing and Printing. . . . The greatest part of the Paper-Mills are mostly employed in making Brown-Paper, which is made of Coarse Raggs, and useless Rope-Stuff serviceable only for that Occasion.

War with France was followed by the prohibition of all trade in French manufactures in 1689, and a great scarcity of paper, among other things, in England. The scarcity gave English paper-millers a strong inducement to make book-papers, hitherto imported from France; and there is reason to think that many of them turned over from coarse to fine milling at that time.[3]

There are indications that early attempts at making white

---

[1] Possibly it was circumspection about the monopoly that prevented Wolvercote Mill from using distinctive watermarks for a time after the formation of the company. John Beckford, miller c. 1695–1726, put no watermarks in the paper traceable to him on the faith of the Press Accounts, excepting that for the *Grammar* of 1709, which has the French bunch of grapes but no initials.

[2] B.M. Harl. 5942 (17).

[3] *Collected Papers of Rhys Jenkins*, Camb. U.P. for the Newcomen Soc., 1936, p. 178.

paper in this country often ended in failure. The Company of White Paper Makers itself has an obscure history and did not long survive.[1] It is mentioned in the existing accounts of the University Press only twice, as delivering paper to the value of £304. 18s. in 1692 and 60 reams in 1694.[2] A memorandum addressed to John Locke, as Commissioner for Trade, in 1696 alleging 'Reasons why the Paper Manufacture in England has not succeeded',[3] apparently refers to the Company (printed as Appendix I). In his *Encyclopaedia* of 1738 Ephraim Chambers could still write that 'the English manufacture hitherto has been in no great reputation' (s.v. 'Paper'). Oxford books of the better quality were printed on French and Italian papers until the middle of the century;[4] but the outlet that the University Press and licensed printers provided for book-papers made at the neighbouring mills for use in books of lesser account must have given these mills an advantage until the expiry of the Licensing Act in 1695 allowed printers to set up businesses in other provincial towns besides Oxford and Cambridge.

[1] The best account of the Company is in W. R. Scott, *The Constitution and Finance of English, Scottish and Irish Joint-Stock Companies to 1720*, iii (1911), 65–70. There was a royal proclamation of 1687 threatening penalties on 'evil-disposed persons, foreigners and others', who tried to entice away its servants and forbidding the export of linen rags. ('For the encouraging and better establishing of the manufacture of white paper in England', 29 April 1687.)

[2] The Account for Printing, 1690–1708, pp. 2, 46 (CP).

[3] Bodl. MS. Locke C. 30, fo. 43.

[4] For the drawback of import-duty on paper for learned books and Bibles, see Appendix V.

III · THE ERA OF HAND-MADE PAPER
AND THE FIRST MACHINE

N the surrender of Fell's lease in 1690 the University of Oxford began to print by direct labour, owning its own plant. It had done so for a short time (1669–71) after the failure of Robert Scott to finance Beveridge's *Synodicon* and before letting its privileges, plant, and premises for printing to Fell and his three partners. From 1690 onwards the accounts of its warehouse-keepers, unfortunately concerned only with 'learned books' (excluding Bibles), record its purchases of paper and sometimes the names of the suppliers. Wolvercote is first mentioned in the accounts for 1694, when 119 reams of foolscap, costing 5s. 6d. a ream, were delivered to the Learned Press by Mr. Quelch of Woolvercott.[1]

People of his name are recorded as living in Wolvercote from 1657 until 1695,[2] and as millers and paper-makers elsewhere at much the same time. Bartholomew Quelch, miller of Rotherfield Peppard, where paper was made later, if not then, died in 1672;[3] John Quelts was a miller at Sutton Courtenay in 1654 (and the mills there made paper by 1693),[4] and Thomas Quelch, miller of Henley-on-Thames, died in 1710.[5] Edward Quelch was one of the 'Ancient Paper Makers of this kingdom' who signed a petition in 1690 against the incorporation of the Company of White Paper Makers.[6] In Kent, the most flourishing centre of English paper-making, James Quelch is believed to have occu-

---

[1] The Account for Printing, 1690–1708, p. 46 (CP).
[2] Parish registers; Hearth-tax returns, P.R.O., Exch. Lay Subsidies, 164/504, m. 43 (1662); 1665, printed in Oxford Record Soc. xxi. 117.
[3] Berks. County Records, D/ER T81.
[4] Ibid.   [5] Bodl. MS. Wills. Oxon. 290.
[6] *Hist. MSS. Comm., 13th Report, App. Pt. 5, House of Lords MSS., 1690–1*, p. 76.

pied a mill at Dartford about 1698,[1] and William Quelch was a paper-maker at Dartford, Loose, Wrotham, and Hollingbourne between 1723 and 1741.[2]

The surname Quelch is traceable back to 1558 in Bensington;[3] and it was, perhaps, from there that it spread to other places along the River Thames. The eldest to bear it in Wolvercote was probably John Quelch, senior, victualler, who died there in 1672;[4] and the first of the name who seems likely to have occu-

Watermarks attributable to Thomas Quelch of Wolvercote Mill in Edward Pococke's *Commentary on Hosea*, Oxford, 1685. The original is 3 inches high.

pied the mill was Thomas Quelch, father of a daughter baptised in 1657. It was probably he who delivered paper to the University Press in 1694.

The historians of the day, Bullord and Bagford, have handed down a story about the beginnings of paper-making at Wolvercote that is not confirmed by the surviving records. There is a third source of information: the thing itself speaks. A book printed at Fell's press in the Sheldonian Theatre in 1685 has

---

[1] I am indebted to Dr. D. C. Coleman, of the London School of Economics, for this information.

[2] See A. H. Shorter, 'Early Paper-Mills in Kent', *Notes & Queries* (21 July 1951) cxcvi. 309.

[3] Index to Wills, &c., in the Archd. Court, Oxon., Bodl. MS. Wills, Oxon. 290.   [4] Bodl. MS. Wills. Oxon. 290; MS. Ch. Oxon. 2598.

some sheets watermarked with the initials T. Q.[1] It is reasonable to conclude, therefore, that Thomas Quelch of Wolvercote was making book-papers by that time.

The part played by George Edwardes, the engraver, in the establishment of the manufacture, may have been like that played at the neighbouring mill at Eynsham by George Hagar, a London dyer. Hagar was granted a patent in 1682 for his improved method of making white paper by sizing the pulp in the mortar.[2] In a subsequent lawsuit his counsel said he could prove that he had 'Set up some paper mills at Ensham and elsewhere' before 1691.[3] The miller at Eynsham at that time was Thomas Meale,[4] and there is no trace of Hagar in local records. Edwardes at Wolvercote, like Hagar at Eynsham, was probably a middleman, who had some part in improving the processes used at the mill, but was not a miller.

The evidence suggests that Thomas Quelch, who was living in Wolvercote by 1657, added the making of coarse paper to his business of milling flour before 1674, and that the mill had begun to make white paper for books in 1683.

Within three years of the disappearance of the last Quelch from Wolvercote records, that is to say in 1698, John Beckford makes his appearance in them as a father. The next trace of paper from Wolvercote at the University Press is the payment to Mr. Beckford in 1708 of £38. 14s. for 86 reams of crown paper at 9s. a ream for the 'Oxford Grammar' (*A Short Introduction of Grammar of the Latin Tongue*, Oxford, at the Theater, 1709).[5] References to John Beckford in the diary of Thomas Hearne, the Oxford antiquary, explain who he was. On 27 September 1718 Hearne noted:[6]

[1] E. Pococke, *A Commentary on the Prophecy of Hosea*, Oxford, 1685, folio.   [2] P.R.O., Privy Seal Dockets, Ind. 6755, p. 129.
[3] *Hist. MSS. Comm., 13th Report, App. Pt. 5: House of Lords MSS., 1690–91*, p. 496.
[4] *Wise and others* v. *Jordan* (1686), P.R.O. Chanc. Proc., Mitford's Div., B. 345, No. 179.
[5] The Account for Printing, 1708–47, fo. 7 (CP).
[6] *Hearne's Collections*, vi. 1902 (Oxf. Hist. Soc. xliii), 231.

In Wolvercote, or rather Wolvescote, Church-yard are buried several of the children of John and Elizabeth Beckford. The said John Beckford & his wife are now living at Wolvercote Paper Mill. He is famous for making Paper. Some of the best Paper made in England is made at Wolvercote Mill. But much the best Printing Paper in England is made at Southampton by a Frenchman.

The University bought 26 reams of paper from Beckford in 1714 to print its 'Verses on the Queen's Death' (*Pietas Univer-sitatis Oxoniensis in Obitum Serenissimae Reginae Annae et Gratulatio In Augustissimi Regis Georgii Inaugurationem,* 1714).[1] In 1715 £6 worth of paper was bought from Beckford for 'Verses on Dr. Radcliffe's Death'[2] (*Exequiae Clarissimo Viro Joanni Radcliffe M.D. ab Oxoniensi Academia solutae,* 1715). The quality of Wolvercote paper can be judged by these samples: and it is an excellent, thin, crisp paper of an even composition, but, alas, with no watermark that might help to identify paper from the same mill in other books of Beckford's day.

At this time Beckford was also making paper for the Bible Side of the Clarendon Building, then let by the University to John Baskett. An inventory of Baskett's stock in 1720[3] includes a 'Minion Bible 12°' then being printed, for which 'Paper is furnished by Mr. Beckford of Woolvercutt and Mr. Thomas Meale of Ainsham' and 'A Brevier Testament 12mo, Comon Sort, always printing, for which four hundred Reams of paper is now sending down by Mr. Stewart and at other times fur-nished by Mr. Beckford, Mr. Rich, etc.'

John Beckford died in 1726; and noting his death, Hearne adds a little to our knowledge of him by another entry in his diary.[4]

Dec. 3. Mr. John Beckford of Wolvercote, who died of the Gout in his Stomack on Wednesday Night last, was buried in Wolver-

---

[1] Account for Printing, 1708–47, fo. 39 (CP).
[2] Ibid., fo. 48.
[3] Assignment of mortgage, Brooke and Baskett to Latane, 23 May 1720 (P).
[4] *Hearne's Collections,* ix, ed. H. E. Salter, 1914 (Oxf. Hist. Soc. lxv), 230–1.

cote Church to-day. He would have been compleat fifty nine Years of Age had he lived till twelfth day next, he being born in the Year 1667, at Drayton, near Dorchester in Oxfordshire.[1] His father is buried in the Chancell of Wolvercote Church, & so is a younger brother of his, viz. Thomas Beckford, who died of the Gout some years since, in the 44th Year of his Age. Mr. John Beckford hath left a Widow and four children, & is died rich. . . .

His eldest son, John, aged 20, was admitted a freeman of the City of Oxford by hereditary right on the death of his father,[2] and it may have been he who carried on business at the mill. Eighty-five reams of demy paper at 10s. a ream were bought by the University Press in 1733 of Mr. Beckford for printing 'the Grammar' (the last Oxford edition of William Lily's *Latin Grammar*, written soon after 1500).[3] But thereafter it was a Mrs. Beckford who is found supplying the University Press. In 1734, 1735, and 1738 she was paid at the rate of 8s. a ream for crown paper to be used in the occasional verses with which the University honoured royal births, deaths, and marriages.[4]

There is no further trace in the accounts of the Press of paper-making at Wolvercote after 1738 for fifty years, the suppliers of the Learned and the Bible Presses of the University during that time being London stationers. But documents belonging to the Duke of Marlborough show that paper-making went on at the mill, at any rate at intervals, throughout the eighteenth century. William Faichen applied for a 21-year lease in 1752 of Woolvercutt paper-mills and corn-mills, offering a rent of £31 a year and an outlay of £200 on mending the roof and walls. Faichen was in occupation until 1771, when the duke agreed to grant a new lease to Thomas Pearson, 'late of Dulcott in the County of Somerset, papermaker', of the house, paper, and corn-mills with engines, vats, and press.

[1] Wolvercote parish registers show that there were Beckfords there as early as 1674.
[2] *Oxford Council Acts, 1701–52*, ed. M. G. Hobson, 1954 (Oxf. Hist. Soc., N.S., X), p. 161.   [3] Account for Printing, 1708–47, fo. 48 (CP).
[4] Ibid. Dr. A. H. Shorter has found a record of Mary Beckford as conducting the business in 1743.

Whether or not corn was ground and paper made in one building, the two kinds of milling were clearly conducted by one man. It is impossible to say whether it always had been so since paper was made at Wolvercote; but it is clear that both businesses went on until the last years of the century. Pearson wished to give up his lease, and a new one was granted in 1773 to Robert Wakefield, of Oriel College in the University of Oxford,[1] and David Ogilvy, of Datchet, Bucks., mealman. No more is heard of the mealman, but things went badly for Wakefield, and in 1779 a distress was levied on his goods at the mill, among them 'a considerable quantity of paper of different sorts in the Sole, Vatt and Drying Rooms', a horse and cart, and two boats. Wakefield held on for three years, and then by consent an inventory was taken of his belongings at the mill, and estimates were got for a thorough reconditioning of the buildings, machine, and weir.

The inventory lists equipment for paper-making (see Appendix II) and flour-milling on a small scale, the whole valued at £98. Wakefield was equipped with moulds for printing and writing papers of eight sizes from double crown down to pott and among the rest a sizing-copper and alum-box. The millwrights' estimates were for building a pound-lock near King's Weir at a cost of £248, repairing the weir for £100, and new installations for flour-milling, and, to a less extent, for the paper-mill. The water-wheel, by inference, served both businesses: the new one was to be 16 feet in diameter and 'four feet wide of the Ladle', costing £7. 7s. for work and £8. 13s. for timber (ladles were the projecting fins outside the framing of the wheel on either side). For paper-making the biggest item was a new 'hurst' for the beaters to work on (a floor to the beating-trough): it was to be made of 20 stones, each 6 feet by 3 feet by 1 foot, and this, said the millwright, 'would make an Exceeding Good foundation'.

---

[1] There is no trace of him in the *Alumni Oxonienses* or the *Registers of Oriel College*. Perhaps he was a servant of the College.

How much of the work was done is not recorded: certainly no lock was built, this being the first of many projects for a lock to get no further than the estimate. The succeeding tenant, William Jackson,[1] at whose request the inventory had been made, was a prominent business man of Oxford. He was the proprietor of *Jackson's Oxford Journal*, a printer, bookseller and stationer, and one of the founders of the Old Bank. Two years before taking his lease of Wolvercote Mill he had joined with the University and Archibald Hamilton in a partnership for conducting the Bible Press. The partnership was a new venture, due to the impossibility of finding anyone in 1780 willing to lease the University's right to print the Bible and the Bible Side of the Clarendon Press building previously occupied by Baskett and other lessees. In the new partnership the University reserved to itself the controlling share, but looked to Jackson and Hamilton for the initiative and technical supervision necessary for the success of the enterprise. The system lasted until 1883; and credit for the expansion of the Bible-business during its first fifteen years must be given mainly to Jackson, who looked after its affairs in Oxford, whilst Hamilton was the London partner.

For the eleven years, 1782–93, therefore, the mill had this personal link with the press of the University; and yet no evidence can be found to prove that paper made by Jackson at Wolvercote was used for Oxford Bibles. The accounts of the partnership show no payments to him for paper, though they record a sum paid by the partners for rags in 1785 and one for a pair of fine wove moulds in 1787—items which suggest that paper-making was among their activities. At this time the largest payments for paper were made to Wright, Gill & Co., stationers of London; and it would appear that superior Bibles were printed on foreign paper got from them. Nevertheless, it

---

[1] Duplicate land-tax assessments in the records of Quarter Sessions, County Record Office, Oxford; Church-Wardens' Accounts in the Wolvercote parish registers. For Jackson there seems to be no source of biographical information other than Nichols's *Literary Anecdotes*, iii. 398, 679.

is possible that the cheaper books from the Press were done on paper from Wolvercote. It seems safe to attribute to Jackson's management of the mill a large demand from the University and its partners for Wolvercote paper in the years following his tenancy.

Jackson gave up the mill in 1792–3, some two years before his death, and was followed by John Swann,[1] one of a family that made paper at several mills near Oxford for at least four generations. Swann enlarged the mill more than once, and built up a

A watermark attributable to John Swann of Wolvercote Mill in a leaf of foolscap paper used for writing the duplicate land-tax assessment of the parish for 1799 (Oxfordshire County Record Office). Reduced by one-third.

large business (by the standards of that time) with the University Press. He bought Eynsham Mill for his brother James in 1804–5,[1] and between 1792 and 1840 Swann Bros. were by far the largest, and for some years the only, suppliers of paper to the Bible and Learned Presses.

In the accounts of the Press Swann first appears in 1788;[2] but where he was working at that time remains to be discovered. His tenancy at Wolvercote began five years later, and within three years he submitted to the landlord a 'Proposall for Improvements at Woolvercutt Mill', dated from Woolvercot Paper Mill, 27 March 1796.[3] John Swann wrote:

---

[1] Land-tax assessments, as above.
[2] Bible Press Account books (CP).   [3] At Blenheim Estate Office.

There being at this Mill a power of Water more than adequate to the Works now upon it, and the Proprietors of the Clarendon Press, Oxford, being desirous of engaging a larger supply of Paper than can in its present state be manufactured at it, the Tenant begs leave to submit to His Grace the Duke of Marlborough the following proposal. He will undertake to encrease the manufactry from a two to a four vat Mill on having a lease granted for 31 years and rough timber found for the alterations. The timber necessary will be 60 loads, and the Tenant will engage to spend £900.

John Swann's improvements put an end to the corn-mill. They included roofing part of the building with tarred paper, a product of the mill at Eynsham and highly praised for dura-

Watermarks of John Swann in the Oxford demy-folio Bible of 1799. The original is 6 in. high. The 'lily and bend', originally a Strasbourg watermark, was by this time conventionally used in demy sheets.

bility and economy by the famous gardener, J. C. Loudon (*An Account of the Paper Roofs used at Tew Lodge, Oxon.*, 1811). John Swann was granted a 31-year lease at £91 a year on 2 April 1799 of 'a dwelling-house and Paper Mill as lately improved, late a corn-mill' with 8¾ acres of land adjoining.[1] Swann's lease-

---

[1] At Blenheim Estate Office.

hold took in the Crown ale-house, the fine old dwelling still facing the mill across the street, and its Home Close of $2\frac{1}{4}$ acres; moreover, he was a grass-farmer on a large scale, renting Picksey Meadow at £96 a year and Ensham Meadow at £25. By 1802 a second large rebuilding, costing Swann a further £1,000, had been completed, and the shape of the mill during the next half-century was attributable to this enterprising man. For financial help he was indebted to William Hall, brewer of Oxford, and William Dawson, a partner with the University in the Bible Press, who kept the Oxford Bible Warehouse in Paternoster Row, London. Swann was associated also with a fellow of Queen's College, John Barwis, who lived for a time at the Mill House and evidently took an interest in the business.[1]

Besides Swann, Stephen Faichen, of Eynsham Mill, was furnishing the Clarendon Press at this time. He was probably the son of William Faichen, who had once rented Wolvercote Mill, and a native of Wolvercote: in 1785 he became miller at Eynsham and carried on business there until in 1804–5 John Swann bought the mill and installed his brother, James, there.[2] In 1778, for the first time, the University's Delegates for the Press decided to lay in stocks of paper for their learned books (instead of buying specially for each edition). They invited tenders from six London stationers, and gave one of them, Durham, the contract for regular supplies of 'three kinds of good and substantial papers'.[3] On the demise of the stationer in 1798, Messrs. Swann and Faichen were invited to submit specimens and tenders for a wove royal 63 lb. of two qualities and a wove and an 'open' demy 46 lb.[4] After 1805 for nearly thirty years Swann Bros. were the sole suppliers of paper to the Press: in 1814 their bill to the Bible Press was £19,073, and to the Learned Press £1,003.

[1] Letter from J. Barwis to Jas. Blackstone, 21 Sept. 1812, at Blenheim Estate Office (largely about Barwis's hope of getting the Vinerian Fellowship); letter from W. Cobbett to Jas. Swann, 7 Jan. 1807; Bodl. MS. Eng. Hist. C. 33, fo. 14.   [2] Land-tax Assessments, County Hall, Oxford.
[3] Delegates' Orders, i, fo. 196 (CP).   [4] Ibid. ii, fo. 51.

John and James Swann were on friendly terms with William Cobbett, the radical M.P. and journalist,[1] and they supplied paper for his *Weekly Political Register* on long credit; presumably, therefore, they were in sympathy with Cobbett's political views. When John Swann died in 1806, Cobbett wrote a letter of condolence to James at Eynsham.[2] James helped the widow of John Swann to carry on business after her husband's death.[3]

James Swann was a pioneer in the making of paper by machinery. He and John's widow were the first licensees of Fourdrinier's patent for a machine to make paper.[4] James probably installed his first machine at Eynsham soon after the grant of his licence in 1807, and four years later he asked the eminent mechanical engineer, Bryan Donkin, to make improvements to his machine and to call at Wolvercote Mill with a view to erecting a similar machine there.[5] A 60-inch machine, sold in 1848, was probably installed at that time, and equipped with a coal-fired boiler and steam-engine.[6]

Three generations of his descendants followed John Swann at Wolvercote.[7] In 1818 C. J. Swann writes to the Duke of Marlborough from Wolvercote, asking for a new lease long enough to justify him in modernizing the mill, offering as an alternative to buy the freehold. 'The paper trade', he says, 'is so much

---

[1] Bodl. MS. Eng. Hist. C. 33. For memories of the Swann family at Eynsham, see Sir E. Chambers, *Eynsham under the Monks*, Oxf. Rec. Soc., 1936, pp. 86–87.

[2] Bodl. MS. Eng. Hist. C. 14. I have been unable to find that Cobbett carried out his intention, expressed in the letter, of putting an obituary of John Swann in the *Register*.

[3] Letter from Jas. Swann, at Eynsham, to Jas. Blackstone, 7 Sept. 1808, at Blenheim Estate Office.

[4] *Report from the Select Committee on Fourdrinier's Patent*. House of Commons Paper No. 351, 1837, p. 37.

[5] I am indebted to Mr. R. H. Clapperton for this information quoted from Donkin's diaries.

[6] A letter from Tatham & Co. to Thos. Mallam, 18 Nov. 1848, makes it clear that the machine and steam-plant had lately been sold: Mr. H. Minn's Misc. IIa, County Hall, Oxford.

[7] John Swann succeeded his father in 1806, and was succeeded by Charles Swann in 1819. James followed in 1823. Land-tax assessments, ibid.

changed from what it was when the mill at Wolvercote was built, and the mill is besides so out of repair, that it would require a very considerable sum of money to put it on a par with the many mills which have been lately built.' But the 31-year lease granted in 1799 ran its course, and a new one was taken by James Swann.[1] He succeeded to the lease of Wolvercote Mill in 1823, and in the same year he bought Sandford Mill, on the river below Oxford, where he is believed to have made wrapping-papers.[2] In 1842 and 1844 the paper-maker at Wolvercote was John Swann.[3]

The account of Swann Bros. with the University Press dwindled after 1835 and ceased in 1847.[4] A year afterwards the firm went bankrupt, and its assets at Eynsham, Sandford, and Wolvercote were sold.[5] In 1849 the Duke of Marlborough offered the freehold of Wolvercote Mill for sale by auction,[6] but it remained his property and untenanted until 1855.[7] William Swann became a partner in the paper-making firm of Swann & Blake, at Eynsham,[8] and continued to sell large quantities of rags or half-stuff to the mill at Wolvercote until 1861.

A water-colour drawing by John Buckler, dated 1826, is the earliest record to give an idea of the layout and size of the mill.[9] It is taken from the path beside the mill-head, and gives a view of the north side of the building. Part of the Mill House can be

---

[1] These papers are at Blenheim Estate Office.

[2] Land-tax assessments, County Hall, Oxford; *V.C.H. Oxon.* ii. 240.

[3] *Pigot's Nat. and Comm. Directory,* 1842; *Pigot's Royal Nat. and Comm. Dir.,* 1844.

[4] Wolvercote Mill Cash Account-book, 1855–69 (P).

[5] *V.C.H. Oxon.* ii. 240.

[6] Bodl. G. A. Oxon., b. 92 (36).

[7] County of Oxford (Clerk of the Peace), Toll Bridge, Wolvercote: Statement of the Case *ex pte.* the County, 1874 (printed paper). Papers about the University's case are extant (CP).

[8] *Post Office Directory, 1854.* The information for this directory (so far as Oxfordshire is concerned) is believed to have been collected in 1847: E. E. Cordeaux and D. H. Merry, *Bibliography of Printed Works rel. to Oxfordshire,* 1955 (Oxf. Hist. Soc., N.S., xi).

[9] See the frontispiece. The original and two drawings by Buckler of Sandford Mill are in the possession of the Printer to the University.

seen on the left; the mill spans the stream and has a large wing projecting northward from the main block. The ground floor was taken up by work-rooms, the rag-rooms for picking the rags, the engine-rooms for breaking and beating them, the machine-room where the paper was made, and the salle for sizing, inspecting, sorting, pressing, and baling the paper. All the upper floor is a drying-loft whose outside walls are louvres that can be opened more or less to suit the weather.

Of the buildings in Buckler's drawing only the Mill House is left, and even that has been much altered since he drew it. The old mill was pulled down in 1855 and the new one was built about 75 feet farther north.

A plan of the mill with its lands and a description of them were printed in the particulars of the proposed sale by auction of the mill to be held on 10 July 1849.[1] The plan shows a building answering to Buckler's drawing, the Mill House attached to the east wall of the mill. The mill and the house are described as:

Lot 1. All those Capital Freehold Mills, known as the Woolvercot Mills, the greater part of which are Extra Parochial, comprising an Engine House, fitted up with 2 Water Wheels, and a pit and Fly Wheel to each, working 2 Cast-iron Washing and Beating Engines, with Rollers and Plates. A Rag Duster with Shaft and Rigger, 2 Pairs of Cast-iron Pumps, with Cranks and Wheels, 6-inch Piping to well, and also Lead Piping to the Engines, and from thence to the Stuff Chest.

A Dwelling House, in the Parish of Woolvercot, attached, containing on the Ground Floor a Counting House, Study, Parlour Kitchen, and other Domestic Offices, also on the First Floor a large Drawing Room, 3 Bed Rooms with Dressing Rooms to each and 5 Attics over.

It is confusing for an historian to find that in his edition of *Reliquiae Hearnianae*, of 1857, whose preface is also dated in that year, the University's Keeper of the Archives, Philip Bliss, pays this handsome tribute to Mr. (James) Swann (on p. 414):

[1] There is a copy in the Bodleian Library; G.A. Oxon., b. 92 (36).

The paper on which the present work is printed was made by the proprietor of Wolvercote mill: nor can I do otherwise than recommend to all who desire to inspect an establishment of this nature in its fullest perfection, to pay a visit to my friend Mr. Swann, whose skill and intelligence in his business are only exceeded by his courtesy and good nature in private life.

By this time Mr. Swann had been gone from the mill for nine years. The explanation of this anachronism is that the first 576 pages of the book were printed in 1822–3, when the editor suspended work on it until 1856.[1]

---

[1] S. Gibson and C. J. Hindle, 'Philip Bliss, Editor and Bibliographer', *Oxf. Bibl. Soc. Proceedings and Papers*, vol. iii, pt. ii (1932), pp. 19, 20.

IV · THOMAS COMBE AT THE
MILL HOUSE

> We are now about to visit a manufactory, the hum
> of whose machinery blends melodiously with the
> song of birds, with the rustling of trees, with the
> gurgling waters of the trout-stream, with rural sights
> and sounds, pleasant to the eye and refreshing to
> the soul.
>
> (C. Tomlinson, *Illustrations of Useful Arts
> and Manufactures*, 1858, section on 'Paper'.)

HOMAS COMBE, Superintendent of the Clarendon
Press (also known by his title of Printer to the University) at Oxford from 1838 until his death in 1872,
bought Wolvercote Mill with its Mill House, gardens,
cottages, close, osier-beds, and eyots in 1855.
The purchase was a simple transaction in law, but complicated in equity; that is to say, many people besides Combe had
an interest in it. He was a partner in the Bible Press, a partnership in which the University had the controlling share. The
Managing Partners, three at this time, were business men, who
managed the concern and divided the profits with the University according to the amount of their contribution to its capital.
In its dealings with 'the Partners' the University was represented by a Bible Committee of its Delegates of the Press.

Not long before Combe's purchase of the mill, the chairman
of the Bible Committee, Dr. Cardwell, drew up a memorandum,
headed 'Plan to be proposed to the Delegates of the Press'
(printed at the end of this book as Appendix III).[1] It may be
summarized as an offer by Combe to buy the mill property (at
a very reasonable price) out of his own money and let the
partners, he being one, use the mill for the purpose of their
business, whilst he occupied the Mill House.

[1] A draft in Cardwell's hand is at the Mill.

[32]

The Mill House (left) and Foreman's Cottage seen from the garden (before 1883)
Photograph by J. H. Stacy

Portrait of Thomas Combe by J. E. Millais, 1850. Painted at the Clarendon Press. Panel, size 12¾ × 10¼ in. *Ashmolean Museum, Oxford*

The Delegates, who represented the University's five-sixths share in the partnership, thought carefully before committing themselves; but after three meetings they decided that the scheme should go through.[1] Philip Bliss, University Registrar at the time, who attended the meetings but had no voice at them, left on record his strong disapproval of the decision and regretted that his opposition to it had been ineffectual.[2] Accordingly, the plan was carried out: the Duke of Marlborough conveyed the mill property to Thomas Combe on 14 August 1855.[3]

During the two following years the mill was completely rebuilt and equipped at a cost of £15,000, seven and a half times the figure proposed in the 'plan' submitted to the Delegates.[4] The new mill buildings were put about 75 feet farther north than the old, partly on the old garden of the Mill House, so that the house no longer shared its west wall with the mill, and what had been the yard of the mill was turned into a riverside garden for the Mill House.[5] A public footpath providing a short cut from the mill to the Toll Bridge, on the way to Godstow and Wytham, cut the garden in two, and robbed it of privacy and amenity. The path was stopped by an order of the Justices in 1856 at a cost to Combe of £20 in fees.[6]

Paper-making in the new mill began two years after the purchase; and its history will be traced in the next chapter.

Combe bought the mill, according to his friend Holman Hunt, the artist, because at that time he was afraid that the exclusive right of the Queen's Printer and the two Universities to print Bibles and Prayer-books would soon be taken away

---

[1] Delegates' Orders, 1853–81, p. 13 (CP).

[2] *Oxf. Bibl. Soc. Proceedings and Papers*, vol. iii, pt. ii, p. 236.

[3] The part of the indenture of conveyance made for the Rev. Alfred Hackman (remainderman to uses barring dower) is preserved at the Press (CP).

[4] The lowest tender for the building, by Fisher, of Abingdon, of £3,695, was accepted. The chimney was built by another contractor. The Fourdrinier machine cost £7,000. The steam-plant was by Park, of Bury. The new buildings eventually cost £6,723.

[5] Delegates' Orders, 1854–67, p. 17 (CP).

[6] Certified copy of the order, Trinity Sessions, 1856, with a receipt for the fee (CP).

D

from them. He thought that in a competitive market even the small saving in cost of paper that might come of owning their own mill would be a great advantage to the University and the partners.[1]

Combe paid the cost of the site: that is to say the useless old mill buildings and the cottages and land that went with them; he also paid half the cost of the new buildings, while the University and partners paid the remaining half.[2]

Combe appears to have believed, and to have convinced his partners, that the enterprise would benefit them. He was clearly an excellent man of business, and his judgement deserves respect; and if it seems difficult to understand how paper-making on such a small scale could be economical, it has to be remembered that in 1855 there were only 275 paper-making machines in England, and the great majority of the 328 mills existing at the time worked like the one at Wolvercote—with a single machine or with none.[3]

Holman Hunt went on to say that Combe bought the mill with his own money because he proposed to satisfy himself that it could be worked profitably before handing it over to the Bible Press partnership.[4] But it is hard to believe that he can ever have meant to finance and conduct the paper-making business himself; and the purchase of the property by Combe is best explained as a speculation on his part aimed at supplementing and safeguarding his share in the Bible-business and an inducement to his partners to follow his lead into paper-making. The plan put to the Delegates (Appendix III) is evidence that he wanted the Mill House to live in; but the surviving papers do not make it clear that he ever lived there. To understand the transaction it is necessary to know something of Combe's character and circumstances.[5]

[1] W. Holman Hunt, *Pre-Raphaelitism and the Pre-Raphaelite Brotherhood*, 1905, ii. 182.   [2] Letter, W. G. Mallam to T. Combe, 28 Nov. 1867 (CP).
[3] A. D. Spicer, *The Paper Trade*, 1907, pp. 247, 250.
[4] Hunt. op. cit. ii. 182.
[5] *D.N.B.* (but with caution); notes by Philip Bliss, Bodl. MS. Top. Oxon.

Thomas Combe was born in 1797 at Leicester, where his father was a printer and bookseller. He went to school at Repton, and came to Oxford to work in the printing and book-selling business of Joseph Parker. After some years there, he became dissatisfied because Mr. Parker would not take him into partnership, and he left and went to work in London. He was recommended to the Delegates for the Press by Mr. Henry Parker when the post of Superintendent of the Clarendon Press fell vacant in 1838; and on 24 June in that year he was appointed in that capacity.[1] He remained in control of the Press until his death in 1872; and he was the main influence on the develop-ment of printing at Oxford during that time. The press was then divided in two, each with its own manager, the Learned or Classical Side, directly controlled by the University, and the Bible Side, in which the partners had an interest with the University. Combe was admitted as a partner in the Bible Press in 1841, with a holding of two and a half of the total of forty-eight shares.[2] He continued to superintend printing on the Learned Side in the interests of the Delegates as well as on the Bible Side on behalf of the Partnership. In 1853, when the two older partners died, Combe became the senior partner, and increased his holding to eight shares.

When Combe joined it, the Bible Press was a very profitable business. Nearly half the Bibles, Prayer-books, and Church Service-books produced in England were printed at Oxford. In 1820 the output of the Bible Press was roughly 750,000 books, and it rose steadily to an average of a million a year by 1865. Two-thirds of the output of Bibles and Testaments was sold to the British and Foreign Bible Society; and the demand from the society and the booksellers was mainly for the cheapest

e. 270, p. 45; *In Memoriam T.C.*, Oxford, privately printed (1872); A. T. Bassett, *S. Barnabas', Oxford*, Oxford, Mowbray, 1919; *U. of Oxford: Ashmo-lean Museum: Catalogue of the Combe Bequest*, Oxford, privately printed, 1909; recollections of J. W. Embury in *The Clarendonian*, i. 66 (July 1919).
[1] Delegates' Orders, 1811–53, p. 257 (CP).
[2] Bible Press Cttee Minute Book, 16 Feb. 1841 (CP).

possible product. The progressive lowering of the price of what were called 'Common' Bibles went on until, in 1864, one in 24° was being sold to the Society for 4d. a copy. These very low-priced books were the main product of the Press; and little by little the profits dwindled, and by 1860 it had become a much less lucrative concern.

But Combe, coming into the business at a good time, made a great deal of money in his first ten years as a partner; and he was able thereafter, whilst remaining a hardworking Superintendent of the Press, to indulge tastes in private life for which he is chiefly remembered.

When he first came to Oxford he lived with an unmarried sister, who rented a house in Oriel Street and let lodgings to members of the University. J. H. Newman and Pusey were among her lodgers, and Combe came very much under their influence; he listened to their sermons at St. Mary's and read the Tracts. In 1840 Combe was married by Newman, who some years before had introduced him to his future wife. He started a Sunday School for the boys at the Press, where he taught regularly for more than twenty years besides giving evening classes in secular subjects. He was a generous supporter of the church and church schools of St. Paul, near the Press; he gave a large contribution towards the rebuilding of Wolvercote Church in 1857, and he built a schoolroom for the mill at his own cost in the same year, on the site of the present offices of the mill. He presented the chapel of the Radcliffe Infirmary in 1859. In 1869 he founded, and bore all the cost of building, the Church of St. Barnabas, for the district of Jericho, whose development was stimulated by the building of the Clarendon Press in Walton Street in 1827–32. Combe's circle of friends took in a number of clergymen of the Anglo-Catholic persuasion.

In 1848 J. E. Millais was introduced to Mr. and Mrs. Combe; and in the following year he stayed with them in their house in the quadrangle of the Press whilst he painted Combe's portrait. Millais wrote them letters for several years which show that he was fond of them both, and he brought them in touch with other artists of the Pre-Raphaelite school.[1]

Combe began buying the work of this school in 1850, with Holman Hunt's 'Converted British Family Sheltering a Christian Missionary from the persecution of the Druids', and his important collection of their paintings and drawings, excepting Hunt's 'Light of the World', was bequeathed to the Ashmolean Museum by Combe's widow in accordance with his wish. Mrs. Combe gave the 'Light of the World' to Keble College, and built a chapel for it.

Holman Hunt, in particular, was a close friend of Mr. and Mrs. Combe, and in his memoirs, *Pre-Raphaelitism and the Pre-Raphaelite Brotherhood*, he praises them and their kindness to him very warmly.[2] One of his anecdotes, told as testimony to the royal memory for faces, throws light on another of Combe's pursuits.[3] Hunt painted a crowd on London Bridge celebrating the wedding of the Prince of Wales and the Princess Alexandra, and put in the crowd several of his friends. The prince came to see the picture, and pointing to a face no larger than a sixpenny-piece, he said: 'I know that man! Wait a minute—I have seen him in the hunting-field with Lord Macclesfield's hounds. He rides a clever pony about fourteen hands high, and his beard blows over his shoulders. He is the head of a house at Oxford, not a college—yes—I remember now. It's the printing-press.'

Hunt's love of the meadows about Godstow may have led Combe's inclinations towards the Mill House. 'There was a mill then out of use at Wolvercott', Hunt wrote, 'and we wended our way there not infrequently in the character of searchers after the picturesque.'[4]

No literary evidence has been found to strengthen the pre-

[1] J. G. Millais, *Life etc. of J. E. Millais*, 1902, i. 87–105, *et passim* to 209.
[2] Hunt, op. cit. ii. 409–12.   [3] Ibid. ii. 244.
[4] Ibid. iii. 183–4.

sumption that Combe entertained his Pre-Raphaelite friends there as he did at his other home in the Clarendon Press; and a report that Hunt 'painted on his "Hireling Shepherd"' (1851) in a garden at Wolvercote refers probably to a little replica of the original painted about 1855.[1] But he did give a party there to the men and boys of the Press, about 150 strong, on 30 June 1855.[2]

The mill property was twice enlarged in Combe's lifetime.[3] In 1864 he bought the Mill Close and the Foreman's House from Worcester College, and in 1871 two cottages fronting on the village street adjoining the Foreman's House. On 29 October 1872 Combe sold the whole property to the University at a price representing his outlay and compound interest at 3 per cent. Ten days later he died suddenly in his house at the Press.

[1] According to a note at the Press (P), C. P. Boyce, the artist, recorded this in his diary under 18 Aug. 1862; see Hunt, op. cit. ii. 184.
[2] Cox and Timberlake's (overseers') Note-book (P, No. 32), p. 56.
[3] Deeds in possession of the Delegates.

'Mrs Pat', a quick drawing of Mrs. Combe by J. E. Millais in his album at the Ashmolean Museum. 'Pat' was short for 'Patriarch', a nickname for Thomas Combe.

V · THE MILL UNDER THE PARTNERS

ECITALS in the lease from Combe to the University's Solicitor, executed in February 1856, declared the intention of the parties to pull down the existing mills and build new ones with a steam-engine and other machinery suitable for a paper manufactory. Comparison of the plans of the buildings in the title-deed of the property in 1855 and of Mill Close in 1864 shows a great increase in the size and an entirely new siting of the mill. A tender for the building by Messrs. Fisher, of Abingdon, of £3,695, was accepted and the work was finished within a year: the first consignment of paper to the Bible Press from the new mill was delivered in February 1857.[1]

The Fourdrinier machine installed in 1856, making a sheet 72 inches wide, worked until 1940, and alone until 1898. No hand-made paper was produced at the new mill.

The partnership system lasted until 1883, and was extended to the Learned Press in 1862. The partners subscribed a separate capital for working Wolvercote Mill and kept separate accounts for it. They resolved in 1857 that the mill could not be worked economically without making more than the University Press could use, and agreed that the surplus might be sold.[2] There is evidence that paper was supplied to the Queen's Printer, the British and Foreign Bible Society, and Messrs. Clowes for Bibles printed elsewhere.

At the time of Combe's purchase of Wolvercote Mill, the University Press was supplied mainly by Messrs. Dickinson. The Bible Press bought paper to the value of £15,000 from Dickinson's in 1856, and the Learned Press about £100 worth. Other paper-makers sold the Bible Press £6,250 worth in the

---

1 Bible Press, Paper Journal, 1854–81 (P).
2 Delegates' Orders, 1854–67, p. 27 (CP).

same year: the Learned Press paid Cowan's £233 and Venables £25.[1]

The ruling prices were 9d. or 9½d. a lb. for fine papers, 9d. for thin Bible paper (13 lb. or 14 lb. a ream demy), 8d. for thickei Bible paper, and 7d. for 'seconds'.

The new mill at Wolvercote supplied the Press with 123 tons of paper in its first year, and charged £17,576. It began by selling fine paper at 8½d. and seconds at 7d., but before the end of the first year the prices went up by a halfpenny. The discount for prompt payment was 2½ per cent., whereas the outside suppliers allowed 5 per cent.[2]

From the first the new mill specialized in making Bible paper, whose peculiar characteristics were thinness and opacity. The problem of cheapening the Bible was the main preoccupation of the partners, for they were dependent on the Bible societies for more than half their sales, and the production of 'Common' Bibles rose steadily as the demand for 'Fine' ones fell. Paper was two-thirds of the total cost; and a saving on Bible paper would have helped more than anything else to bring business into the Press and make it profitable. John Dickinson, the paper-maker, of Nash Mills, Hemel Hempstead, recorded a visit from Combe in 1852, aimed at getting cheaper paper to enable him to compete with Scotch Bibles, selling for a penny less than the English.[3]

For the lowest-priced Bibles it was necessary to buy paper from Belgium or France; the English mills were too dear. But from 1857 until 1900 Wolvercote Mill supplied the Press with practically the whole of its requirements for a product of medium quality, rising gradually from 120 to about 300 tons a year, or three-fifths of the maximum output of the mill. The available records do not show that ownership of the mill meant a saving in the cost that the partners had to bear for paper:

---

[1] Bible Press, Paper Journal.
[2] Ibid.
[3] Joan Evans, *The Endless Web*, 1955, p. 68.

from 1856 until 1866 it remained constantly two-thirds of the total cost of production of Bibles (excluding composition). The cash accounts of the mill for the years 1855–69 are extant.[1] They show that the University and partners subscribed £21,500 in 1855–6 to pay for the building and machinery and provide a working capital. During the ten years 1858–67 receipts from trading exceeded expenditure by an average of £2,425 a year, and dividends averaged £2,020. After 1864 profits fell to an average of £2,110 for the next five years and dividends to £980.

The demand from the Bible Press was increasingly for cheap paper, and as time went on the amount of fine paper made at Wolvercote diminished. In 1865 the Bible Press took 6,334 reams of fine paper and 19,455 of seconds: in 1870 the figures were 3,038 reams of fine, 5,808 of seconds, and 24,793 of third-quality Bible paper. Third-quality was first made in 1859, and it remained until 1880 the principal product of the mill. For the cheapest Bibles and Testaments Wolvercote was too dear: in 1863 and 1864 a Belgian mill, Godin's, of Huy, supplied paper at $4\frac{1}{2}d.$ a lb., which was $\frac{3}{4}d.$ less than the lowest Wolvercote price. In 1879 a Lancashire firm succeeded in lowering the price to $3\frac{3}{4}d.$, the lowest recorded for a book-paper in the history of the Bible Press.

After cheapness the quality most sought after in Bible paper was thinness; and in the attempt to achieve it without too much sacrifice of opacity there were interesting developments at Wolvercote. In 1853 Thomas Combe experimented with printing a Bible on a paper weighing 7 lb. a ream, foolscap, made by Fourdrinier's of Hanley.[2] It was so thin that, in order to get over the problem of the print showing through, the sheets had to be printed on one side only and the leaves of the book doubled. In its early days Wolvercote Mill regularly made thin Bible paper weighing 10 lb. a ream, and even delivered 2 reams of fine Bible

---

[1] Account book, No. 41 (P).
[2] 'Mr. Combe's Memoranda on Paper for Bibles, dated 1853' (P).

paper weighing 6 lb. in October 1858. This must have been for
an experiment, and no such thin paper was made there again
until 1875. After 1864 even the 10-lb. paper ceased to be made,
and thereafter the thinnest Wolvercote paper weighed 14 lb. a
ream. Apart from the slowness and excessive waste of handling
sheets as thin as this, rag paper was by nature too transparent
to be made in such very thin sheets for use in books.

Extremely thin, tough, and opaque paper of the kind that
came to be known as 'Oxford India' was tried at the Press as
early as 1842. Combe printed twenty-four copies of the Bible in
24° format on a paper of this kind in that year.[1] The experiment has become a legend at the Press and the truth about it is
hard to discover. No copy of the 24° Bible appears to survive,
but there were several in existence in 1900 (one was exhibited
at the Paris Exhibition, 1900). The following account of the
origin of this paper was given by Henry Frowde, the Publisher
to the University, in 1900:[2]

In the year 1841, a small fold of extremely thin paper was
brought to England from the Far East, which was manifestly more
opaque and tough for its substance than any paper then manufactured in Europe. This paper sufficed for the printing of exactly
twenty-four copies of the smallest Bible then in existence. (*Paris
Exhibition, 1900. Oxford University Press Paper Exhibit, Oxford,
&c. 1900.*)

Another writer, in 1911, added that the sample sheets had
been brought from China by 'an Oxford graduate' and continued:

Combe failed to trace the paper to its source. Among many persons applied to was Mr. Gladstone. . . . His reply is still preserved,
recommending a search in Japan. From Japan papers were obtained, but though equally thin and tough, they were too trans-

---

[1] *Oxford Univ. Press: Paper Exhibit, Paris 1900*, London (H. Frowde) 1900,
p. 11; *Notes and Queries*, No. 65, 25 Mar. 1911, p. 221. 'The Smallest Complete
Bible, on India paper, date 1816' was exhibited at the Caxton Memorial
Exhibition, 1877: *Caxton Celebration 1877: Catalogue*, p. 189.

[2] *O.U.P. Paper Exhibit, &c.*, p. 11.

parent, and could not be printed on both sides. Afterwards a paper was produced at the mills of the Press, but it was far too yellow.[1]

However, it is clear from one of his letters to Bartholomew Price, written in 1894, that Frowde's printed account of the origin of Oxford India paper relied on oral tradition. 'I have always understood', he wrote, 'that the original edition of the small Bible consisted of twenty copies which Mr. Combe printed on a small quantity of paper that came from China.'[2]

A paper-maker, who examined the small Bible in 1896, was of opinion that the paper was machine-made of English origin and belonged to the class known to the trade as 'Pottery Tissue',[3] which Fourdrinier was making at Hanley before 1837.[4]

However that may be, it was from Pottery Tissue that Oxford India paper was developed later; and it is clear that as early as 1853 Combe was aware of the advantages of 'Pottery' paper for overcoming problems of bulk.

In 1853 Combe was asked to estimate for a Bible in Chinese for the British and Foreign Bible Society. The number of pages involved must have been very great, for he reckoned that it would take five years to print at a rate of 10,000 sheets a day. He told his overseer to write to Mr. Arnett for specimens of Pottery paper.[5]

John Arnett was the son of a former manager of the Bible Press. He too served his apprenticeship there as a compositor; but he left Oxford 'with Mr. Mulock, the leader of a religious sect; went with him into Staffordshire, and became a partner in the firm of Pratt & Co., potters and earthenware manufacturers. He married Miss Pratt.' He died in 1876 aged 71, a few months

[1] J. C. Francis in *Notes and Queries*, loc. cit. A sheet of the first trial-making from Wolvercote has been preserved at the University Press.
[2] Letter of 29 Jan. 1894: Constance Meade Collection, Papermaking I (P).
[3] F. Haigh, of Brittains Ltd., to H. Hart, 30 Oct. 1896: Portfolio of 'India Paper: Ancient History' (P).
[4] *Report from the Select Cttee. on Fourdrinier's Patent*, House of Commons Paper No. 351, 1837, p. 35.
[5] Cox and Timberlake's (overseers') Note-book (P, No. 32), p. 26.

before his brother, who was Manager of the Bible Side at the Press.[1]

It was probably the connexion with Arnett that made the Press acquainted with a type of paper made of rope, very thin and tough, supplied to potters but never before used in book-printing.

Nothing more is heard of oriental or of Pottery paper at the Press during Combe's lifetime: it was two years after his death, that is to say in 1874, that interest in it revived. Henry Frowde, then Manager of the Oxford Bible Warehouse in London, saw one of the Bibles of 1842, and moved the Press and the mill to find a supply of a similar paper.[2] On being asked, the Manager of the mill, J. H. Stacy, at once wrote to Thomas Brittain & Sons, successors to the Fourdriniers at Ivy House Mill, Hanley, who undertook to match the paper used in 1842.[3] Samples were sent to him in March 1875, and the first consignment, 8 reams, followed in June and was used to print another experimental edition of the Bible in the smallest format.

Brittains described themselves as makers of Pottery and other thin copying and transferring and stereo tissue-papers. The head of the firm in 1896 thought that paper of a character much like Oxford India had been made at his mill long before 1875.[4] Definite and contemporary evidence about the origin of the paper is lacking, but Henry Frowde was certainly mistaken in later years in saying that this type of paper was first made at Wolvercote and made at that time nowhere else.

Wolvercote Mill began to make India paper at this time. Samples of their work and of Brittains' with Stacy's comments dated 1875, have been kept.[5] The Wolvercote sample is yellower than the one from Hanley. It appears from the accounts[6] that Wolvercote Mill delivered 209 reams of this paper, named at

---

[1] Cox and Timberlake's (overseers') Note-book (P, No. 32), pp. 115–16.
[2] J. C. Francis in *Notes and Queries*, loc. cit.
[3] Letter from F. Haigh, 30 Oct. 1896, cited on p. 43.
[4] Ibid.   [5] Printer's archives.
[6] Bible Press, Paper Journal, 1854–81 (P).

that time 'Diamond 24° Bible *thin*', in December 1875, and Brittains delivered 50 reams. It would seem that the Wolvercote making was not altogether satisfactory: no more was delivered after April 1877, and ten years later the University was negotiating with Brittains for instruction in making India paper.

The India Paper Bible of 1875 was a success: 'within a few weeks a quarter of a million copies were sold'.[1] Wolvercote delivered 276 reams of their thin paper in 1876 and 22 reams in 1877. Bills from Brittains came to these amounts:[2]

					£
1877	.	.	.	.	408
1878	.	.	.	.	—
1879	.	.	.	.	555
1880	.	.	.	.	1,556
1881	.	.	.	.	1,992
1882	.	.	.	.	1,249
1883	.	.	.	.	1,150
1884	.	.	.	.	3,847
1885	.	.	.	.	1,670
1886	.	.	.	.	3,892
1887	.	.	.	.	5,154

By 1887 the paper was in such great demand that Brittains had to face the choice between enlarging their mills or losing the monopoly of the business. That it was a monopoly shared by the Press and Brittains is clear from the recitals in a formal agreement reached with them in 1888:

That for several years past [Brittains] had been making special thin opaque printing paper for the Oxford University Press, used for their 'Thin India Paper' editions, and that business between them has been done on the understanding that [Brittains] would supply this paper only to the Press, and that the Press would not make it or buy it elsewhere. . . .[3]

[1] *O.U.P., Paper Exhibit, &c.*, p. 12.
[2] Memo. from H. Hart to the Secretary to the Delegates, 13 Dec. 1887: Portfolio of 'India Paper: Historical' (P).
[3] Rough draft of Proposed Agreement (Dec. 1887): ibid.

It is also clear that one term in the understanding was that the Press might sell the paper elsewhere. The first of such consignments from the Bible Press that can be traced is one of 22 reams to the London Warehouse in 1880,[1] where Mr. Gardner, one of the partners, had undertaken the sale of it in addition to his trade in Bibles. By the end of 1882 the Press at Oxford had begun to supply large quantities to Desclée, Lefebvre et Cie, liturgical printers of Tournai, Belgium.[2]

It is said that the furnish of India paper was kept secret even from the workmen, and for many years its sale was a monopoly of the University Press. In this century paper of the same kind has been supplied by mills in Italy and Germany, but when they began to make it is not known. The India paper made at Wolvercote was of two kinds: demy 9 lb. and demy 6 lb.

The introduction into printing of India paper was among the successes achieved by the Press under the leadership of Professor Bartholomew Price. This Doctor of Divinity and Professor of Mathematics had been appointed a Delegate in 1861, and Secretary to the Delegates in 1867. He was the architect of the modern University Press: little by little he converted it from a factory for cheap Bibles and a few learned books into the greatest publishing-house and one of the largest and best-equipped presses in the world. Steps in this progress were these: in 1862 the Bible and Learned Presses were merged; in 1863 the publishing business was entrusted to Mr. Macmillan; in 1867 Professor Price became Secretary; in 1869 the University acquired a binding business and began to bind its Bibles; in 1872 he annexed to his office the duties of Chief Manager of the Press; in 1880 the University ended its agreement with Mr. Macmillan and undertook its own publishing; in 1883 the last of the partners was bought out and the first salaried Controller was appointed to the printing press.

How Professor Price regarded the mill as a business proposi-

---

[1] Bible Press, Paper Journal, 1854-81 (P).
[2] Correspondence in the Portfolio: 'India Paper: Ancient History' (P).

tion does not appear from surviving records; but under his régime it underwent no reforms of organization and he did nothing to enlarge it or alter its character. Its single machine went on producing papers of the kinds needed by the University Press, among which Bible paper predominated. Confidence in the future of paper-making at Wolvercote is proved by the purchase of Baker's Close, a meadow of $3\frac{1}{4}$ acres on the east side of the property, in 1875.[1]

Credit for the smooth running of the mill and efficiency such as to satisfy Professor Price must be given to the Manager, John Henry Stacy. He was appointed in 1855 at a salary of £400 and a house, the Foreman's Cottage, next door to the mill.[2] Stacy's contract of service, renewed in 1867 and 1881, was ended only by his death in 1883. In 1867 he invested a substantial amount in the Clarendon Press, and thereafter instead of a fixed salary he was paid one that fluctuated with the profits of the concern. His letters to Professor Price are written in admirable, precise language, and show a keen interest in mechanical engineering; but they betray a grievance about his own position: he was aggrieved because he was not a partner. His later history proves that his ambition to engage in business was a misfortune for him. His irritation worked itself up to such a point that in 1866 he resigned his post, and was coaxed back into it only by the skilful handling of the Secretary. It broke out again in 1872, when he pleaded for admission to the partnership and produced a letter denying him membership of the Paper Makers' Club because he did not occupy the position of a master. The Club, as it seems, was a forum for discussion and resolution of problems facing the trade, an embryonic association of masters.

Stacy secured a partnership in the Press in 1872, thereby exposing himself to periodic demands for contributions to

[1] Note by J. H. Stacy, 4 Nov. 1875 (M); the conveyance of 1876 is among the title deeds (CP).
[2] Stacy's letters are at the mill and in the 'Combe Box' (CP).

increases of capital which he could meet only by borrowing. Under the new dispensation following the death of Thomas Combe, Stacy undertook the duties of Superintendent of the Clarendon Press in addition to the management of the mill.[1] In 1876 he objected to an item in the partnership accounts, and, after an altercation lasting many months and reference to expert opinion, which went against him, he gave up his post at the Press and confined himself to management of the mill for the rest of his life.

Among other things Stacy was a good amateur photographer. A number of his photographs, taken at and around the mill, were sent to the present Controller by his daughter, Miss Mary Stacy, of Karlsruhe, in 1953, nearly a hundred years after her father's appointment to Wolvercote Mill.

---

[1] Cox and Timberlake's Note-book, p. 115 (P)

J. H. Stacy, Manager of Wolvercote Mill, 1855–83, in a group. The photograph, which belonged to Stacy, can only be dated by the costumes—about 1865

A group photographed at the front door of the Mill House, 1871: (left to right) Prof. Bartholomew Price, his sister Mrs. George, her son Hereford George, Thomas Combe, Mary Beck, Miss Abbott, Mrs. Price.

Photograph by I. H. Stacy

VI · RECENT HISTORY

TACY's death in 1883 was the beginning of a new era in the development of the University Press. The belief expressed, for example, by the Royal Commission on Cambridge University of 1852, that no committee of dons 'however active and well-chosen can replace the intelligent and vigilant superintendence of those whose fortune in life is dependent upon its success',[1] had lost its hold on the Delegates during the secretaryship of Professor Price: they bought the shares of the surviving partners, and, assuming the entire reponsibility for the management of the printing business, appointed Horace Hart as Controller of the Press. In London, Henry Frowde had been since 1880 the first salaried Publisher to the University. At Wolvercote, also, partnership was abolished, and Joseph Castle, trained as an engineer and later employed as machine-room overseer at the Clarendon Press, was appointed Controller.[2]

Both Frowde in London and Hart in Oxford took a keen and expert interest in paper: Castle, on the other hand, seems to have been an engineer by inclination as well as by training, and he allowed Hart, particularly, to guide him towards the introduction of new kinds of paper and their treatment at the mill.

Publishing as distinct from the printing of privileged books now became the spearhead of the business; and it forced the pace for the printing-press and the mill. The number of editions from the University Press increased steadily; but a much greater increase of output was due to the changed character of the secular books. Besides comparatively small editions of learned works, the University had begun about the middle of the century to sponsor cheap standard texts and educational

---

[1] Parly. Papers, England, 1852–3, No. 44, p. 137.
[2] Obituary in The Clarendonian, ii. 34 (July 1921).

books in large numbers. Dictionaries, beginning with Liddell and Scott's *Greek Lexicon* of 1841, also became important in determining the character of the Press. By the time of Castle's appointment the business of the University Press had ceased to be almost exclusively in cheap Bibles and had become that of a general book-printing house.

Wolvercote Mill had to adapt itself to the altered demand. Before 1890 it had ceased to make India paper,[1] and it began making large quantities of medium-weight printing papers of a mixed rag and wood-pulp content, sold by the name of 'Wolvercote Mill'. About that time, also, it had produced its first sample of 'All-Sulphite' paper for tracing and draughts-man's work. Esparto-grass was never introduced at Wolvercote.

The development of India paper reached a point in 1887 where Brittains were unable with their existing resources to make as much as the Press wanted, whether for their own use or for sale. The head of the firm, Thomas Brittain, decided against taking steps to enlarge the output; and instead an agreement was reached on 30 October that Mr. Frederick Haigh, of Brittains, reputed at that time as the only man who could make India paper well, would help the University to establish the manufacture at Wolvercote.[2] An extension of the mill was contemplated by the agreement, and Castle suggested buying the water-mill at Hampton Gay that had once belonged to Venables.[3]

Mr. Haigh visited the mill and discussed the technical diffi-culties with Horace Hart and Castle.[4] The processing of India paper involved so much lime that the effluent would kill all the fish within two or three miles of the point of discharge. Even-tually this difficulty proved insuperable, and there is no reason

---

[1] Letter from J. Castle to P. Lyttelton-Gell, 13 July 1892 (M).
[2] Correspondence in Portfolio of 'India Paper: Historical' (P).
[3] Finance Cttee. Minutes, 24 May 1887 (CP). Charles Venables first occu-pied this mill in 1817: Land-tax assessments, County Hall, Oxford. It was offered for sale, vacant, in 1849: Bodl. G.A. Oxon. b. 85a (32).
[4] Notes by H. Hart dated 9 and 10 Nov. 1887: 'India Paper: Historical' (P).

to think that more than token quantities of India paper were made at Wolvercote thereafter.[1]

In 1889 old Mr. Brittain's objection to the enlargement of his business was withdrawn, and the younger members of his firm were keen to make all the India paper that the Press could use or sell. They bought a second mill at Cheddleton, Staffordshire, and by an agreement of 1894 they made sure of the exclusive right to supply the Press and its customers and promised not to market the paper themselves. There was a proviso that Wolvercote Mill might make India paper with the consent of Brittains Ltd. if the company were unable to supply enough of it.[2] A vigorous campaign for the foreign sales of this paper was undertaken by the Press in 1890, and met with some success: in 1900 Henry Frowde in London had twenty-two customers for it and Horace Hart at Oxford had seven.[3]

About that time an even greater technical innovation took place in printing and paper-making: the introduction of 'Dry' papers. Before their introduction it had been the practice to wet the sheets of paper before printing and to hang them up to dry afterwards: the whole of the top story of the Clarendon Press building of 1827–32 was devoted to drying-rooms for printed sheets. The sheets of the best and most expensive books were glazed after printing and drying.

Horace Hart wrote a memorandum for the Delegates, dated 30 October 1889, on 'Glazed paper from Wolvercote for "dry" printing'.[4] Dry paper, he said, was thin glazed paper for Bibles and Prayer-books, and it came into use at Oxford in 1887. Bibles printed on this paper at Cambridge were in circulation in 1886, and were much liked by the Bible societies (though not by Mr. Frowde). 'I learned', Hart wrote, 'that the Cambridge paper was procured through Messrs. Sabel, of 85 Cannon Street,

[1] Finance Cttee. Minutes, 13 Nov. 1890 (CP).
[2] The Agreement and correspondence leading to it are in the Portfolio 'India Paper: Ancient History' (P).
[3] Memo. in Portfolio of 'India Paper: Modern History' (P).
[4] Portfolio in Cupbd. B, No. 8 (P).

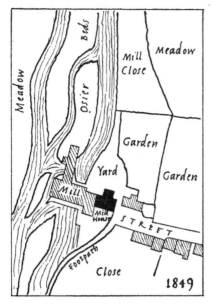

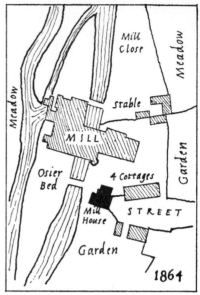

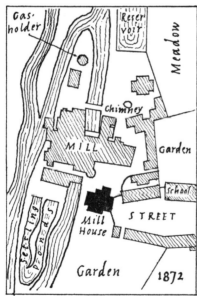

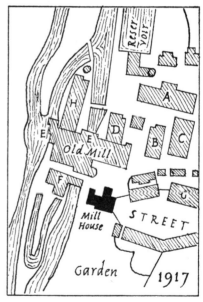

Plans illustrating four stages in the growth of the mill: 1849, 1864, 1872, and 1917.

A. New Machine-room	E. Water-wheels
B. Glazing-room	F. Pulp and chemical stores
C. Paper warehouse	G. Paper warehouse (old school)
D. Beating-room	H. Pulp and coal stores

who are agents for the great Belgian house of E. L. Godin et fils, of Huy, near Liége, where the dry paper is made and glazed.' The Bible Press at Oxford bought paper of this kind to the value of £21,288 from Sabel in the years 1887–9 and the relation of Bibles printed dry to those printed wet in 1888–9 is shown by the deliveries to the London Warehouse, not including lectern Bibles or those on India paper: Wolvercote paper: 789,456; Dry paper: 1,276,616.

In 1888 Hart and Castle went to Huy and obtained entrance to Godin's mill. It ran night and day seven days a week and could deliver paper at Oxford at the price of $3\frac{1}{2}d$. a lb. 'There is great force', Hart thought, 'in the argument that Bibles and Prayer Books should not be printed on paper made by working on Sunday. We ought to be able to make at Wolvercote all the kinds of paper used at the Press.' The obstacle was that the mill, for lack of enough glazing-machines, was unable to supply this paper.

Hart went on to say: 'I hear in London that such improvements have been made in the treatment of wood-fibre that we can now use paper made of that material and highly glazed.' He thought it premature at the time of writing to predict the supersession of rag papers printed damp; but he felt sure the new Dry paper made from wood had proved its value.

Wolvercote began to make Dry paper soon afterwards; but its glazing-machines were capable of dealing with a maximum of 500 reams a week, and the demand from the Press by 1892 was for twice as many. Castle urged on the Delegates the need for more glazing capacity. Even the sabbatarian argument failed to move them to a quick response: and it was in 1896 that the decision was reached to instal super-calenders, which were less good but easier to staff than plate-glazing machines.[1]

Enlargement of the mill followed two years later. The Delegates came to it reluctantly. They were told that the average

---

[1] Letter from J. Castle to Lyttelton-Gell, 13 July 1892 and others in Env. 184 (M).

weekly output of the mill was 11 tons of paper.[1] The Press
was then using 12 tons of cheap Bible paper a week, and was
expected to increase its demands to 18 tons before long. The
Delegates needed another $1\frac{1}{2}$ tons for learned books, and the
Publisher in London wanted some for export to America. No
other paper-maker, even in Belgium, was willing to supply the
Press with Bible paper as good and as cheap as Wolvercote
paper, which was costing the mill $2\frac{1}{2}d$. a lb. to make and was
sold to the Bible Press at very little more than cost price. The
unsatisfied demand and the lower costs to be expected from
increased production argued in favour of the proposed enlargement: the high cost of motive power (available water-power
being fully used) and the increase of the effluent (already caus-
ing much concern) were arguments against it. Mills in the
north and midlands were buying coal at half the price delivered
at Wolvercote. But in October 1897 a committee of the Delegates recommended enlargement:

> The Committee being of opinion that it is to the advantage of
> the Press in all its Departments that the Delegates should be in
> possession of a Paper Mill sufficient for the wants of the Businesses,
> it is resolved that Mr. Castle be instructed to prepare plans and
> obtain estimates and specifications for the enlargement of the
> Mill as suggested by him, and in particular as to the relative cost
> of steam and gas motors.[2]

The plans providing for a second Fourdrinier machine, new
steam-power, and the new buildings needed for doubling the
work of the mill were passed in May 1898.[3] Castle himself was
architect as well as engineer of the new works.[4]

The building was done in 1898, and the new machine making
a sheet 80 inches wide was installed in 1899, the whole cost
being nearly £20,000.[5] The 'New Machine', as it was called, is
still running. The 'New Mill' buildings were very much bigger

---

[1] Finance Cttee. Minutes, 7 Oct. 1897, item 10 (CP).
[2] Ibid. 13 Oct. 1897 (CP).   [3] Ibid. 12 May 1898 (CP).
[4] Obituary, *The Clarendonian*, ii. 34.
[5] Note dated 24 May 1899 (M).

The mill built in 1855–6, seen from the south. *Photograph by J. H. Stacy*

Joseph Castle (left), Controller 1883–1916, with work-people from the mill. Taken before 1890, and sent to Miss Stacy. The three in the middle are John Stone, carter at the mill, and his wife and son. On the right is Charles Morris, the colour-mixer. The women were employed at the mill as rag-pickers than the 'Old Mill' of 1856 to which they were annexed. Production rose from 500 tons a year in 1897 to 1,040 tons in 1913.[1]

In the years 1900–14 India paper grew in favour, and its use was extended from Bibles and Service-books to standard works of reference and fiction. In 1912 the University and Brittains Ltd. signed a new agreement designed to promote the manufacture of India paper in large quantities and to increase the sale of it outside the Press.[2] It was made at that time in three grades, costing 1s. 3d., 1s., and 10d. a lb., and the agreement of 1912 provided for the marketing of two cheaper grades, one at 9d. a lb. and another, called 'Enhanced Datum' paper, at 4s. a ream of 480 sheets weighing 7–10 lb. It was agreed that if orders for as much as £5,000 worth were received in three months, the makings of India papers would be shared equally by Brittains and Wolvercote Mill and 'in order to enable the Company to co-operate with the University Press in the manufacture of India paper at the Wolvercote Mills, a nominee of the Company . . . shall be recognised by the Press as joint controller of the Wolvercote Mills and shall . . . have full access to the Mills and to the work carried on in them and to all books and accounts'. Mr. Frederick Haigh, the chairman of the company, was appointed Joint Controller at Wolvercote and given a small honorarium for that service. A year later the Delegates at Oxford were debating a proposal to lease the mill at Wolvercote to Brittains.[3]

Castle, who seems to have worked very willingly with Haigh, was attracted to the idea of separating the business of the mill from the University Press, and for a reason that seems curious. He was troubled by the incursion of trade unionism. It was due, he said in August 1913, to agitation among his workmen by trade unionists in the Press; and he thought (rather strangely) that if the business were renamed 'Brittains Ltd., Wolvercote

---

[1] Undated notes by J. Castle on enlargement of the Mill (1897); J. Castle's Pocket-book, p. 72 (M).
[2] Portfolio of 'India Paper: Modern History' (P).
[3] Correspondence between J. Castle and F. Haigh, July–Aug. 1913 (M).

Paper Mills', the influence of the printers' trade unions upon it would be less compelling. Of 54 men working at the mill in 1913, 46 had joined the union, and so had 15 of 28 women. Castle stopped all wage-increases in consequence.[1]

This appears to have been the beginning of regular organization among the paper-workers at Wolvercote; sporadic attempts at it must have gone back to 1792, for in that year a paper-maker's journeyman was convicted at Oxford of taking part in a strike.[2]

Organization of labour at Wolvercote was completed about 1925. Since then all the employees at the mill have been union members.

The war of 1914–18 put an end to any disposition among the Delegates to part with control of the mill. Production rose in the first two years of the war; but 1917–22 were very lean years in which the mill often stopped for weeks at a time for lack of work.[3]

Joseph Castle retired in October 1916, and died in 1921.[4] He was succeeded as Controller by Mr. A. D. Clapperton, one of a paper-making family, his brother, George, being the tenant of the University at Sandford Mill. The first concern of the new Controller was to find more business: and he began in his first year to make cheap featherweight paper for the children's books of the Press, which at that time were growing rapidly in number.

By the end of the war the machinery and equipment of the mill were run down. The Delegates decided in October 1919 to spend £13,500 on repairs and renewals: only just in time, for two months later the supply of paper was interrupted by mechanical troubles.[5]

[1] Correspondence between J. Castle and F. Haigh, July–Aug. 1913 (M). See also Delegates' Orders, 2904–13, p. 438 (CP).
[2] M. S. Henderson, *Three Centuries in North Oxford*, 1902, p. 107.
[3] J. Castle's and A. D. Clapperton's Notebook, 1883–1947 (M).
[4] *The Clarendonian*, ii. 34.
[5] Finance Cttee. Minutes, 3 Oct. 1919, 2 Dec. 1919 (CP).

A generator for electric lighting and a small supply of power was installed at the mill about 1920. The old paper-making machine was converted to electric drive not long afterwards; but the larger machine was steam-driven until 1938, a steam-turbine being introduced to supply electric power in 1939. Until 1943 the rag-beating engines were still worked by water-power turning three wheels. Since 1939 the paper-making machines have been driven wholly by electricity.

During the war of 1939–45 Wolvercote Mill was one of the first in the country to be equipped with a plant for extracting ink from printed paper. Using re-pulped stuff, it was able to keep up a supply of good book-papers enough for such learned books as could be produced in those days.

A. D. Clapperton was Controller until his death in September 1943. His nephew, J. F. Clapperton, son of Mr. George Clapperton of Sandford, was appointed to succeed him and took charge of the mill on being released from war-service with the Paper Control in July 1945. He died, however, only three years later, and his place was taken by the present Controller.

In the last four years the 'Old Mill', dating from 1856, has been completely demolished; but the machine bought in 1898 is still working in part of the so-called 'New Mill', which survives the recent rebuilding.

The mill offices, built in 1953 to the design of Booth and Ledeboer, F/F.R.I.B.A., are on the site of the old schoolroom built by Thomas Combe in 1857, part of the old walled garden belonging to the Mill House, and four workmen's cottages built in the time of Combe.

This history comes to an end a hundred years after the University's Delegates began to make paper at Wolvercote. For the last century the mill has been equipped to supply the papers that were most in demand for the Delegates' printing and publishing in the quantity that they needed. In that time it was necessary to double the capacity of the machines. That point was reached in 1896; and some years ago the demands of the

Press once more outstripped the supply from Wolvercote. Another enlargement of the mill is almost complete, which will increase its capacity to one considered economical in modern paper-making. The output will be some 240 tons a week (about twenty times the output of 1857), an amount that the Press is not expected to use for many years to come. This change in the character of paper-making at Wolvercote closes the history of a small mill.

Air photograph of the mill and site, 1950.

The Weighbridge House opposite the mill offices, bought by Thomas Combe in 1871.
In 1834 it was known as the 'Crown' ale-house

VII · TOPOGRAPHICAL NOTES ON THE SITE

The Weighbridge House

HE fine old house facing the offices of the mill across the street was described in the Inclosure Award of 1834 as 'the Crown ale-house'.[1] When Thomas Combe bought it in 1871, it and a cottage next door on the west were called 'Hall's Cottages', and a close of land south of their gardens was occupied with the ale-house. The title-deeds belonging to the University show that The Crown came into the possession of the family of Hall, well-known brewers of Oxford, as satisfaction for debts incurred for beer. John Hamilton, of Cassington, cordwainer, bought the house in 1770; his son, described as victualler, mortgaged it in 1813 to William Hall, of Oxford, to secure an unpaid account of £272 for beer; in 1826 the victualler's children sold their interest in the property to the mortgagee. It was from his grandson that Combe bought the house.

The Foreman's House

The last cottage on the left of the village street was occupied by J. H. Stacy, the first manager of the mill built in 1856. It belonged at that time to Worcester College, but Combe bought the freehold in 1864. The close of land adjoining the mill on the east side of the mill-stream went with it. One of the title-deeds belonging to the University, dated 1693, describes the common rights attaching to the cottage when it was conveyed to John Bishop, ale-brewer of Oxford.

One Messuage, Tenement or Cottage, one orchard, one garden

[1] The parish's copy of the Award is now deposited in the County Record Office at Oxford.

and 6½ acres of arable Land in Woolvercott or Woolgercott and one Close lying behind Woolvercott Mill and Common of Pasture for six Beasts in the Commons and Common Fields of Woolvercott, and Common of Pasture in Wolvercott Mead, after the hay thereof is tined yearly for four Beasts, and common for all manner of other Cattle for one Quartern Land in such sort and Manner and at such Times and in such Places as the Inhabitants of Woolvercott aforesaid do common there . . . and also Common of pasture for all manner of Cattle in Port mead and in the Hurst and in the Moor adjoyning to the Town of Woolvercott.

And for safety's sake the lawyer added:

And all houses, edifices, buildings, barns, stables, backsides, orchards, gardens, meadows, leasows, pastures, feeding leys, hades, meers, baulks, ways, woods, waters, watercourses, customs, workdays, rents, services, fishings, profitts, easiaments, advantage, commodities, emoluments, lands, tenements and hereditaments whatsoever to the premises or any part thereof belonging or in any wise appurteyning.

Until the enclosure it was the practice to let the commoners of the village graze their cattle in the water-meadows after the hay had been carried: the meadows were 'tined' (fenced) until that had been done. Similarly, the arable land in the common fields was thrown open for grazing after harvest. The number of beasts that a commoner might turn out on the commons was proportioned to the size of his holding. This house and a close of about 3 acres and 6½ acres of plough-land in several small parcels in the common fields ranked as a quartern of one yardland (Mortgage of 1619), and its allowance of common right was rated accordingly. A full yardland was a holding of some 32 acres, more or less.

Other words in the deed apply to small holdings in open common fields. 'Hades', or headlands, were the ends of plough-lands, where the team turned, and so impossible to cultivate fully unless by hand; 'meers' were plots reserved for boundaries, 'baulks' and 'ways' were strips marking the limits of small holdings or used to gain access to them. All these were used for pasturing tethered animals whilst the crops were growing, and were subject to rights of common pasture after harvest.

'Customs, workdays, rents, services' were put in to pass the right to payments in money, in kind, or in services that might be attached to the holding.

The Toll Bridge

The Toll Bridge at the southern limit of the mill property was known by that name in the reign of Henry VIII.[1] There was a gate at the east end of it in 1855, no doubt to stop cattle from straying off Port Meadow and Wolvercote Moor. Why it is called the Toll Bridge is hard to say; in 1873 great efforts were made to find records or memories of any tolls being paid to cross it, but there were none.[2] It is a very old name; and it is probable that the tolls once paid there were on livestock and goods brought to an annual fair held close by under the protection of Godstow Abbey. The fair was a privilege said to have been granted to the abbey by King Stephen, and the tolls charged on everything brought to it were a source of revenue to the nuns. The little field of two acres next to the bridge on the north-west side was known as 'The Fair',[3] and may well have been the place where it was held.

Anthony Wood, the historian of Oxford University, says that the funeral procession of 'Fair Rosamund' in the time of Henry II halted at the Toll Bridge, where a cross was put up with a Latin inscription inviting passers-by to pray for Rosamund's soul. He says that the fair was held by this cross 'and multitudes of people resorted thereunto'.[4]

---

[1] Dugd. *Mon.* iv. 370.

[2] County of Oxford (Clerk of the Peace): Toll Bridge, Wolvercote: Statement of the Case *ex pte.* the County 1874 (printed paper) (CP).

[3] 'Item a p'cell of grownde next Stonebridge, called the Fayre, which lyeth comen, cont. 3 acres': Dugd. *Mon.* iv. 376; 'le ffayre close' P.R.O. L.T.R. Memo. Rolls, 13 Jas. I, Hil. m. 200. It shrank by the time of the Inclosure to 2 acres and there was a cottage on part of it (still there in 1917).

[4] *Wood's Life and Times*, i, ed. A. Clarke, 1891 (Oxf. Hist. Soc. xix), 338–9.

King's Weir

When the University took over the mill from Combe in 1872 there was still a cottage on the east side of King's Weir.[1] The Thames Conservancy's keeper in 1912 could remember an old woman who lived there sixty years before.[2] She looked after the weir, and boatmen went to her cottage to borrow a lever to work the winches. At that time the weir had a pair of gates exactly like gates of a lock, with sluices in them, and worked by winches and chains. The cottage had gone by 1885, when the Thames Valley Drainage Board bought the weir, but the plot of land on which it had stood was still part of the mill property.

The management of the weir caused a number of disputes. In 1813 one Williams of Wolvercote took legal proceedings against the lessee of the mill for failing to draw up the sluices when the river rose to high-water mark. The offence was proved, and the fine of £10 was divided between the Thames Navigation Commissioners and Williams.[3] In 1823 the Navigation Commissioners

went from Oxford by water. Met Mr. Swann by appointment at King's Weir, examined the Bargemen and others as to the operation of the [weir] upon the Navigation, discussed the subject at length with Mr. Swann.

. . . The Committee find that the work here recommended was done, but that the Sluice Gates have been for some years past useless. They find further that the pen Gates of the river have been very considerably raised above the former level, by which combined causes, in conjunction with Mr. Swann's refusal to draw the water when the necessities of the Navigation require, the Barges are constantly stopped in their progress.

The committee, therefore, recommended that the regulation of the gates should be 'placed under the care of the Commissioner's officers'.[4] But, four years later:

[1] According to the plan in the conveyance (cp).
[2] F. S. Thacker, *The Thames Highway: Locks and Weirs*, 1920, p. 98.
[3] Ibid., p. 97.
[4] Thames Nav. Commissioners, Minutes of the, 29 Sept. 1823: Berks. County Record Office.

It having been stated to the Committee that the sluices which were put in by the Commissioners at King's Weir have been spiked up and rendered unfit for the purposes for which they were intended, it is ordered that the Gen. Surveyor be instructed to put them in order forthwith, and to make immediate report to the Commissioners in the event of their being again injured, in order that the parties may be dealt with according to the utmost severity of the law.[1]

In 1842 Swann put in a new gate at the weir, and the Navigation Commissioners complained that the sluices were about 8 inches higher than those of the old gate and required him to lower them.[2]

A boat-slide was built beside the weir not long before 1872;[3] and, at long last, King's Weir Lock was completed on 29 May 1928.

The Water Meadows

After buying the mill from Combe in 1872 the University added adjoining pieces of land as they came on the market. In 1875 Baker's Close, a plot of $3\frac{1}{4}$ acres behind the cottages to the east of the Mill Close, was bought from the family of Rowland, who had owned it for fifty years. It took its name from the bakery, known in recent years as the Old Post Office, which the University acquired in 1944. In 1722 it was the house and bake-house of Andrew Osborne, baker. Title to Baker's Close goes back to a mortgage of 1617 by John and Ethelbert Weller, yeomen of Wolvercote.

In 1884 the Duke of Marlborough sold his property in Wolvercote by auction. The University bought the island meadows to the west of the mill-stream called Great and Little Baynhams and two small meadows to the north of the mill property on the east side of the stream. Baynhams is a name identifiable with Boieham, part of the endowment of Godstow Abbey in 1404, and described in 1541 as 'pratum vocatum

---

[1] Ibid. 6 Oct. 1827. [2] Ibid. 30 Sept. 1842.
[3] Thacker, p. 99.

Beynams jacens in periculo submercionis aqua singulis annis' (a meadow called Beynams lying in peril of being flooded every year), 'containing 5 acres, worth 2s. 4d. an acre yearly'.[1] Water meadows were surprisingly valuable: the arable land listed in the same survey was rated at 10d. or 8d. an acre. In 1807 John Swann, the tenant of the mill, paid £91 a year for the mill and £92 a year for Picksey Meadow, which adjoins Baynhams on the north.[2] In 1884 the Controller of the mill paid 6s. an acre to have the meadows mown by hand.[3]

The land at the north end of the mill property, also bought in 1884, was named Rowlands Meadow and Little Meadow. Before the enclosure of the parish in 1834 these were part of The Leys. The name Rowland first occurs in the title-deeds in 1834, when Richard Rowland, farmer of Woolvercot, bought 'a little piece of meadow in the Old Leys, 2 roods, 3 perches, which was apportioned to Sarah Collins in lieu of other ground, her property, by Commissioners for inclosing land under Act of 1 & 2 William IV'.

The Duke of Marlborough parted with all his lands in Wolvercote in 1884 excepting an eyot on the east side of the mill-stream close to the Toll Bridge, which he kept to safeguard his right to fish in the stream.[4] It was sold to the University in 1913, and it has since been joined to Webb's Close, the intervening ditch having been filled in.

Rights of Common in Port Meadow

The owner of Wolvercote manor, George Owen, one of the physicians of King Henry VIII, in the name of himself and his tenants, petitioned the king in 1552 against the enclosure of part of Port Meadow by the Mayor and Burgesses of Oxford,

[1] Dugd. *Mon.* iv. 370.
[2] Paper endorsed: 'Executors of Mr. Swann to H.G. the Duke of Marlborough' (1807): Blenheim Estate Office.
[3] J. Castle's Pocket-book, p. 114 (M).
[4] Case for the opinion of counsel on the University's obligation to repair the Toll Bridge, 1874 (CP); conveyance to the University by Mrs. Hector, 1913 (CP).

so as to exclude them from pasturing their beasts there.[1] Commissioners were sent by the Court of Requests to Oxford to hear the evidence of people from neighbouring villages. Owen and his tenants complained that the Mayor and Burgesses on 1 July 'digged and trenched great dyches and Bankis for the inclosure of a gret porcion of Portmede' and had previously enclosed a common pasture named Crypley and allowed some of the Oxford citizens to put sheep on Portmede contrary to custom, so as to imperil the interests of the realm, which demanded the maintenance of kine for tillage. The witnesses confirmed these allegations: they said that the Abbess of Godstow used always to impound sheep that were put on the part of Portmede near Wolvercote, that Wolvercote paid the Bailiff of Oxford 6s. a year, and that Crypley was enclosed by the Mayor's order some twenty years before. There is no record of the Court's decision; but it must have gone in favour of the Wolvercote people, for they continued to common in Port Meadow thereafter.

In 1663 a house and a quartern yardland in Wolvercote entitled the owner to 'common of pasture for three horses or Beasts in Port Meade near Wolvercott';[2] and in 1693 one yardland and three quarters gave the right to 'Common of pasture for all manner of Cattle in Portmead & in the Hurst & in the Moor adjoyning to the Town of Woolvercott'.[3]

[1] P.R.O. Court of Requests, xxiv, 116 (1 May).
[2] Conveyance Collins-Hudson, 15 Chas. II (CP).
[3] Release Brown and others to Bishopp, 1693 (CP).

APPENDIX I

A Memorandum addressed to John Locke in 1696 on the failure of the Company of White Paper Makers (see p. 17)[1]

Reasons why the Paper Manufacture in England has not succeeded.

The Pattentees were men that sett it on Foot & carried it on with noe other design, then to stock Jobb their Shares.

They were allmost all unaquainted wth the nature of white paper makeing, either fine or Printing.

They never made a Reame of Paper wch they sold for ten shillings, but stood them in nearer twenty then tenn for these Reasons.

1. The Rents for and Building of their Mills was more than double what is abroad, or indeede would have bin two hundred miles northward.

2^d The Pay they gave their Workmen was 3 times as much as is given in France.

3^d Their Raggs were sometimes sent by Land Carriage, which that Trade will never afford.

4. The Raggs of [Eng]land are not soe well preserved or gathered as in other Countryes, where all people are more carefull of them, than our Country people are of their Feathers, wch is the Reason y^t a Tonn of French Raggs will make neare double the Vallew of Paper, than a Tonn of English Raggs will, as was tryed about 15 yeares since.

5. They frequently suffered their Mills to Stand Idle, either for want of Judgm^t, mony or Raggs; for if a Mill stand still but 48 hours a month['s] work will hardly recover the damage.

(Endorsed:) For Mr. Locke.
                   Paper Manufacture. Trade. Paper/1696.

[1] Bodleian Library, MS. Locke c. 30, fo. 43.

Inventory of Stock for Paper-making at the Mill, 1782 (see p. 23)[1]

Inventory taken at Woolvercote Paper Mill 19 March 1782 at the desire of Mr. W. Jackson and Mr. Robert Wakefield.

161 foolscap felts
96 Royal hand do
52 Demy   do
133 Double Crown do
   1 pair Double Crown moulds.
   1 pair foolscap   do
   1 pair   do   do (old)
   1 pair Pott.   do
   1 pair   do   do
   1 pair Post   do
   1 pair Large Demy do
   1 pair of writing Demy moulds
   1 pair of Printing Demy   do
   1 pair of Copy   do
Treble Liners.
New Treble Lines.
Rag Hatchet Block and Hurdle.
All the baskets.
All the rag knives.
All the river knives.
1 large tubb.
2 riddles.
Coal shovel, riddle and rake
Fishing tackle.
Siseing copper with ironwork to
   do.

Lines in the Soll
1 pair of shears.
4 iron Bars.
Furnishing pan and Bowle
A wire lates and rag Box
A fish trunk and chain
A cart the harness and saddle.
Siscing box.
Allom box Tongs Sluis and
   Leaver.
3 tables.
1 bucket.
Felt stool and handbarrow
2 Tubbs.
Long leaver Winch 2 Ropes and
   lay stool
3 leavers and a winch rope
Laystool, 1 pair foolscap planks.
Sundry planks, press blocks and
   hook.
A pidgin.
A corn bushell and laystool etc.
   etc.
2 boats and 1 horse.

Total value £98. 4s. 6d.

[1] Original at the Estate Office, Blenheim Palace.

APPENDIX III

Proposals by the Bible Committee of the Delegates of the University Press in 1855 for the acquisition of Wolvercote Mill (see p. 32)[1]

That certain premises at Woolvercot, the property of the Duke of Marlbro', consisting of a Dwelling-house & garden, 3 cottages, a paper-mill & its weirs, water rights & other appurtenances, to-gether with six acres of land & osier bed, be purchased at a price not exceeding £2,000.

That Mr. Combe be the purchaser on his own account.

That Mr. Combe grant a lease of the said premises for forty/fifty years to Mr. F. Morrell to be held in trust by him on behalf of the University & Partners.

That Mr. F. Morrell execute a Declaration of trust on that behalf.

That the in-coming outlay (say £2,000) requisite for the erection of buildings of a steam engine & other apparatus & for putting the premises into good tenantable condition be defrayed in equal proportions by the owner and the occupiers.

That thenceforward the occupiers shall keep the premises in good tenantable repair.

That thenceforward the occupiers shall be at liberty to make any improvements on the premises for the better conducting of their business; but that such improvements shall be at their ex-pense & the Delegates acting for the University shall always have consented thereto.

That the rent shall continue the same for the whole term of years & shall be at the rate of 6 per cent. of the value of the property.

That the value of the property shall be the original purchase money together with the sum paid by the owner as his portion of the incoming outlay.

That Mr. Combe be at liberty to occupy the Dwelling-house &

[1] Original in the custody of the Controller of Wolvercote Mill.

garden together with six acres of land & osier bed as long as he wishes to do so, at the rent of £20 a year.

That this undertaking form part of the original Bible-press concern, & paying over its profits to it but keeping its accounts entirely distinct.

APPENDIX IV

Paper-mills near Oxford in 1816 (see p. 7)

(see p. 7)

THE following is a list of paper-mills in the 'Oxford Collection' of Excise in 1816, given in the General Letter Book No. 4, ff. 22–37, in the Library of H.M. Customs and Excise, London.

Excise No. of mill	Name of paper manufacturer	Mill
257	John Emberlin	Deddington
258	William Emberlin	Newington
259	John Sellers	Hazleford
260	James Swan	Eynsham
261	Charles Venables	Hampton Gay
262	John Evans	Weirs Mill [Oxford]
263	William Drewett	Hinksey Mill
264	James Swan	Wolvercote
265	Unoccupied	Sutton [Sutton Courtenay]

APPENDIX V

Drawback of Import-duty and Excise on Paper allowed to the Universities, 1712–1861 (see p. 17)

In estimating the advantage to the paper-mill at Wolvercote of having a local market in Oxford it is necessary to bear in mind rights granted to the University of recovering duty paid on foreign-made paper. It is true that because of this privilege the presses of Oxford had at times less inducement than printers generally to use paper made in this country.

When paper-making began at Wolvercote imports of paper were subject to a poundage, from which the universities had no relief (12 Car. II, c. 4); and it was not until 1712 that they were put in a privileged position. A statute of that year was the first to make English and Scottish paper subject to an excise, but it continued the import-duty on foreign paper at a higher rate.

Learned books

The statute of 1712 (10 Anne, c. 18, s. 53) gave the universities of Oxford and Cambridge the right to draw back the full amount of duty paid on paper, imported or made in England or Scotland, if it had been used for printing books 'in the Latin, Greek, Oriental or Northern languages'. The account-books of the Warehouse-keepers of the University Press at Oxford from 1716 onwards show sums received by way of 'return of poundage' on paper.

The drawback for learned books was continued by a succession of Acts varying the duties payable on paper until 1861, when the duties were abolished by the Customs Act of 1859 (24 Vict., c. 20, s. 4).

Agitation by the University for the grant of the right to the drawback is proposed in an undated letter from George Hickes to Arthur Charlett: Bodl. MS., Ballard 12, fos. 198 and 198ᵛ.

Bibles and church books

Drawback in full of duty paid on foreign and home-made paper was allowed to the universities and King's Printers of England and Scotland by an Act of 1794 (34 Geo. III, c. 20, s. 39) if the paper had been used for 'bibles, testaments, psalm books, books of common prayer, and confession of faith, and the larger and shorter catechism'. Certain conditions were attached to the privilege, of which one was that the paper must be watermarked with the date 1794 or a later year. The provision as to the watermark was repealed by an Act of 1811 (51 Geo. III, c. 95).[1]

[1] See the article by Dr. C. B. Oldman, 'Watermark Dates in English Paper', *The Library*, 4 Ser. xxv (1945), pp. 70–71.

INDEX

Abbott, Miss, photograph of, *facing* p. 49.

America, sale of 'Oxford India' paper in, 54.

Angoulême, paper made near, 15.

Arnett, John, compositor and potter, 43.

— W., Bible-corrector, 44.

Ashmolean Museum, T. Combe's art-collection given to, 37.

Bagford, John, account of the origin of the mill by, 14, 19.

Baker's Close, 47, 63.

Barwis, John, of Queen's College, 27.

Baskett, John, Bibles printed on Wolvercote paper by, 21.

Baynhams (Boieham, Beynams), meadow, 10, 12, 63, 64.

Beck, Mary, photograph of, *facing* p. 49.

Beckford, family of, at Wolvercote, 20–22.

— John, lessee of the mill c. 1695–1726, 16 n., 20, 21.

Bensington, Oxon., family of Quelch at, 19.

Beveridge, W., editor of the *Synodicon*, 1672, 18.

Bible Committee of the Delegates of the Press, 32, 68.

Bible Press (a part of the University Press at Oxford), 21, 22, 24, 25, 27, 32, 34, 35, 39, 41, 46, 68, 69.

Bible Societies, preference for 'dry' paper of, 51. *See* British and Foreign.

'Black liquor', part of the effluent called, 9.

Blackstone, James, of Woodstock, 27 n.

Bliss, Philip, Registrar of the University, 30, 31, 33.

Boieham, meadow formerly called, 10.

Books, paper for, when first made at Wolvercote, 15, 16, 19–21.

Boyce, C. P., artist, diary of, 38 n.

British and Foreign Bible Society, demand for cheap Bibles from, 35, 36.

— Chinese Bible for, 43.

— Wolvercote paper sold to, 39.

Brittain, T., & Sons (later Brittains Ltd.), India paper made by, 44–46, 50, 51, 55.

— — agreements of the University with, for making 'Oxford India' paper, 45, 50, 51.

— — proposed lease of the mill to, 55, 56.

— — T. Haigh of, 44 n. *See* Haigh.

Buckler, John, drawings by, 29.

Bullord, John, book-auctioneer, 14, 19.

Calendering, equipment of the mill for, in 1896, 53.

Cambridge, University Press at, 17, 51, 71.

Campbell, Mr., of Buscot Park, 4.

Canal, coal brought by, 6, 7.

Cardwell, (Edward), Delegate of the Press, 32.

Cassington Mill, proposal to buy, 7.

Castle, Joseph, Controller of the Mill, 49–56.

Chambers, Ephraim, his *Encyclopaedia* quoted, 17.

Charlett, Arthur, letter to, 72.

Cheddleton, Staffs., paper-mill at, 51.

Chinese, Bible in, 43.

Clapperton, A. D., Controller of the Mill, 56, 57.

— George, of Sandford, 56.

— J. F., Controller of the Mill, 57.

Clarendon Press, Wolvercote paper supplied to, 26. *See* Bible Press; Oxford, University Press at.

Clarendon Press Bible Warehouse, London, 46.
Cloth, mill for fulling, at Wolvercote, 13.
Clowes, Messrs., Wolvercote paper supplied to, 39.
Cobbett, William, a friend and customer of the miller at Wolvercote, 28.
Collins, Sarah, of Wolvercote, 64.
Combe, Miss, sister of T. Combe, lodgings let by, 36.
— Mrs., wife of T. Combe, drawing of, 38.
— Thomas, Superintendent of the Clarendon Press 1838–72, 32–44.
— — additions to the mill property by, 38, 59.
— — his association with Pre-Raphaelite artists, 36, 37.
— — photograph of, *facing* p. 49.
— — portrait of, by Millais, *facing* p. 33.
— — purchase of the mill by, 32, 33, 68, 69.
— — sale of the mill to the University by, 38.
Common rights in Wolvercote and Port Meadow, 59–61, 64, 65.
Company of White Paper Makers, chartered in 1686, 15, 16.
— reasons for the failure of, 17, 66.
Controllers of the Mill: J. Castle, 49; A. D. Clapperton, 56; J. F. Clapperton, 57; J. R. Henderson, 57.
Corn formerly ground at the mill, 13, 16, 22, 23, 26.
Cowans, paper sold to the University by, in 1855, 40.
'Crown' ale-house, Wolvercote, 27, 59.
Crypley (Cripley), pasture called, 65.

Datchet, Bucks., 23.
Dawson, William, partner in the Bible Press, 27.
Deddington, Oxon., paper-mill at, 70.
Desclée, Lefebvre et Cie, of Tournai, 46.
Dickinson, John, paper-maker, 39, 40.

Domesday Book, 11.
Donkin, Bryan, 28.
Drawback of duty on paper allowed to the universities, 71, 72.
Drayton, Berks., 22.
Drewett, William, paper-maker, 70.
'Dry' paper, introduction of, 51, 53.
Duke's Lock, Yarnton, 4.
Dulcote, Som., 22.
Dupin (Duppin), Paul, a promoter of the Company of White Paper Makers, 15.
Durham, a firm of stationers, 27.
Duties on paper, 71, 72.

Edwardes, George, engraver, paper-making at Wolvercote said to have been begun by, 14, 15, 20.
Effluent from the mill, troubles connected with, 8, 9, 50, 54.
Emberlin, John and William, paper-makers, 70.
Embury, J. W., recollections of T. Combe by, 35 n.
English Paper Makers, Case of the, (c. 1690), quoted, 16.
'Enhanced Datum' paper, 55.
Esparto-grass, never used at the mill, 50.
Evans, John, paper-maker, 70.
Excise-duties on paper, 71, 72.
Excise-number of the mill, 70.
Eynsham, Oxon., paper-mill at, 8, 20, 21, 27–29, 70.
Eynsham (Ensham) Meadow, 27.

Faichen, Stephen, of Eynsham, paper-maker, 27.
— William, 1752–71, 22.
Fair at Godstow, 61.
'Fair Rosamund', 61.
Fell, John, Dean of Christ Church, 13–15.
Fish, danger to, from the effluent of the mill, 50.
— King's Weir formerly used for catching, 4.
Fisher, builder, of Abingdon, 33 n., 39.
Fishing-rights in the mill-stream, 64.

'Flashes' of water through King's Weir, formerly required by law, 4.
Footpath to the mill stopped, 33.
Foreman's House, the, 59.
Fourdrinier Bros., thin papers made by, 41, 43.
Fourdrinier machines, installed at the mill, 28, 33 n., 39, 54.
France, paper made in, used at Oxford in the seventeenth and eighteenth centuries, 14, 15, 17.
Frowde, Henry, manager of the Oxford Bible Warehouse, later Publisher to the University, 9, 42–44, 49, 51.
Fulling-mill at Wolvercote, 13.
Furnishing-pan, 67.

Gardner, Edward, a partner in the Bible Press, 46.
George, Mrs. and Mr. Hereford, photograph of, facing p. 49.
Gladstone, Mr., consulted about oriental papers, 42.
Godin, E. L. et fils, of Huy, Belgium, 53.
Godstow, Berks., 1, 4, 10–12, 61, 65.
Grammar of the Latin Tongue, Short Introduction of, printed on Wolvercote paper in 1709 and 1733, 20, 22.

Hackman, Rev. A., 33 n.
Hagar, George, 20.
Haigh, Frederick, of Brittains Ltd., 44 n., 50, 55.
Hall, William, brewer of Oxford, 27, 59.
Hall's Cottages, 59.
Hamilton, Archibald, partner in the Bible Press, 24.
— John, of Cassington, 59.
Hampton Gay, Oxon., paper-mill at, 7, 8, 50, 70.
Hanley, paper made at, 41, 43, 44.
Hart, Horace, Controller of the University Press 1883–1918, 50–53.
Hazleford, Oxon., paper-mill at, 70.
Hearne, Thomas, antiquary, quoted, 12 n., 13 n., 20, 21, 22.

Henley-on-Thames, 18.
Heringeshamme, meadow called, 10.
Hertheshamme, meadow called, 12.
Hickes, George, letter on paper-duties by, 72.
Hinksey, near Oxford, paper-mill at, 70.
Holland, paper-makers sent to England from, 15.
— stationers in, paper sold to the University by, 14, 15.
Huguenot refugees, paper made by, 15, 21.
Hunt, William Holman, artist, association with the mill of, 37.
— — quoted on Combe's reasons for buying the mill, 33, 34.
Hurst, the, pasture in, 60, 65.

Import-duty on paper, drawback of, allowed to the universities, 71, 72.
— statutes regulating, 71, 72.
Inclosure Act for Wolvercote, 59, 64.
India paper, earliest use of, for Bibles, 42.
— 'Oxford', 42–46, 50, 51, 55.
Ink, extraction of, from waste paper, 57.
Ivry, Godfrey d', 11.
— Roger d', 11.

Jackson, William, proprietor of Jackson's Oxford Journal and partner in the Bible Press, lessee of the mill 1782–93, 24, 25, 67.
Jenkins, Sir Leoline, 15.

Kent, paper-makers in, 18, 19.
King's Weir, Godstow, 3–6, 23, 24, 62, 63.

Lambheye (Lambei), meadow called, 10, 12.
Learned Press (part of the University Press at Oxford), 14, 18, 25, 27, 46.
Leys, the, in Wolvercote, 64.
Licensing Act (of 1662), expiry of, paper-making affected by, 17.
Licheseie, meadow called, 10, 12 n.
Lime, fish killed by, 50.

Lincoln, (R. Grosseteste) Bishop of, 11.

Little Meadow, Wolvercote, 64.

Lock, proposals to build, at King's Weir, 6, 23, 24, 63.

Locke, John, philosopher, 17, 66.

London, stationers in, paper sold to the University by, 14, 22, 24, 27.

Loudon, J. C., quoted, 26.

Machines for paper-making. See Fourdrinier machines.

Macmillan, Alexander, publisher to the University, 46.

Madan, Falconer, 13 n.

Marlborough, Duke of, documents about the mill owned by, 22.

— — landlord of the mill, c. 1720–1855, 13, 22–26, 28, 29, 33, 63, 64.

Meale, Thomas, paper-maker at Eynsham, 20, 21.

Medley Lock repaired, 4.

Mill Close, bought in 1864, 38, 63.

— reservoirs in, 12.

Mill House, the, 30, 32, 33, 34, 37, 38.

Millais, Sir J. E., his friendship with T. Combe, 36, 37.

— — portrait of Combe by, facing p. 33.

Moor, the, in Wolvercote, common pasture in, 60, 65.

Morris, Charles, photograph of, facing p. 55.

Moulds at the mill in 1782, 23, 67.

— for wove demy, bought in 1787, 24.

Mulecrophte (Mill Croft), dams in, 12.

'New Machine', the, installed 1899, 54, 57.

'New Mill', the, built in 1898, 54, 55, 57.

Newington, Oxon., paper-mill at, 70.

Newman, J. H., association of T. Combe with, 36.

Northmede, meadow called, 12.

Ogilvy, Robert, of Datchet, 23.

Oilly, Robert d', 10, 11.

Old Bank, Oxford, 24.

Ollei, Robert d', 10, 11.

'Open' (laid) paper, 27.

Oriel College, R. Wakefield of, 23.

Osborne, Andrew, baker, 63.

Output of the mill, 40, 54, 55.

Owen, Sir George, physician to King Henry VIII, owner of the mill, 13, 64, 65.

— — suit about common in Port Meadow by, 64.

Oxford, bailiff of, rent paid by Wolvercote commoners to, 65.

— Canal, 4.

— river Thames made navigable to, 4.

— river-level at, 4, 8.

— University of, beginning of printing by, 18.

— — Bible Press controlled by, 24, 32, 33.

— — control of the mill acquired by, 32, 33.

— — property in the mill acquired by, 38.

— University Press at, constitution of, in 1838, 35.

— — development of publishing by, 49, 50.

— — paper stocked by, after 1778, 27.

— — purchases of paper recorded in accounts of, 18, 20, 21, 22, 24, 25, 27, 39–41, 45.

— — use of Wolvercote paper by, 13, 15, 18–22, 25, et passim.

'Oxford India' paper, origin of, 42. See India paper.

Oxfordshire, paper-mills in, in 1816, 70.

Paper, coarse, ancient manufacture of, in England, 16.

— — early manufacture of at Wolvercote, 13.

— 'dry', introduction of, 51, 53.

— duties on, drawback of, allowed to the universities, 71, 72.

— featherweight, formerly made at the mill, 56.

— for Bibles, special characteristics of, 40, 41.

Paper, foreign, use of, at Oxford, in the seventeenth and eighteenth centuries, 14, 15, 17.
— made at Sandford Mill, 8.
— -making at Wolvercote, beginning of, 13–16.
— prices of, 16, 18, 20, 22, 40, 41, 45, 53, 55.
— sizes of sheets of, made at the mill in 1782, 23, 67.
— tarred, 26.
— wet, formerly printed, 51.
— 'white', early manufacture of, in England, 16, 17, 20.
— wood, made from, when first used at Oxford, 51, 53.
Paper Control, the, 57.
Paper Makers' Club, the, 47.
Park, James, & Co., of Bury, steam-plant installed at the mill by, 33 n.
Parker, Henry and Joseph, book-sellers, 35.
Partners in the Bible Press, the, 24, 32, 33, 35, 39, 46, 47, 49.
Pearson, Thomas, lessee of the mill 1771–3, 22.
Picksey (Pixey) Mead, Wolvercote, 12 n., 27, 64.
Plot, Robert, Keeper of the Ash-molean Museum, quoted, 13.
Pollution of Rivers Act 1876, 9 n. See Effluent.
Port Meadow (Port Mead), common rights of inhabitants of Wolver-cote in, 59–61, 64, 65.
Post Office, the Old, in Wolvercote, 63.
Pottery tissue paper made by Four-drinier Brothers, 43.
— 'Oxford India' paper a variety of, 43.
— tried for a Bible in 1853, 43.
Pratt & Co., potters, 43.
Pre-Raphaelite artists, T. Combe as-sociated with, 36–38.
Price of paper at various dates, 16, 18, 20, 22, 40, 41, 45, 53, 55.
Price, Prof. Bartholomew, Secretary to the Delegates of the Press, 46, 47, 49.

Price, Prof. Bartholomew, photo-graph of, *facing* p. 49.
Prince of Wales (later Edward VII), anecdote about, 37.
Proclamation, royal, of 1687, 17 n.
Pusey, E. B., T. Combe influenced by, 36.

Quartern lands in Wolvercote, 60.
Queen's College, John Barwis of, 27.
Queen's Printers, right to print Bibles shared with, 33.
— Wolvercote paper sold to, 39.
Quelch (Quelts), millers and paper-makers named, 18, 19.
— John, victualler of Wolvercote, 19.
— Thomas, paper-maker at the mill c. 1657–95, 18–20.
— — watermark attributed to, 19.

Radcliffe, John, verses on the death of, 21.
Rags formerly used for paper-making at the mill, 1, 6, 8, 9, 24, 29, 30, 53, 57.
Rich, Mr., paper-maker, 21.
River, the. See Thames.
Rotherfield Peppard, 18.
Rowland, family of, at Wolvercote, 64.
Rowland's Meadow, Wolvercote, 64.

Sabel & Co., paper merchants, 51, 53.
St. Barnabas, Oxford, church of, 35 n., 36.
St. John, John de, 10, 11.
St. Paul, church of, in Oxford, 36.
St. Peter's in the East, Oxford, church of, rights of, in Wolvercote, 11, 12.
St. Waleric (St. Valery), Bernard de, 10, 11.
Salle (Sole, Soll), the, a room in the mill, 23, 30, 67.
Sandford on Thames, mill at, 8, 29 n.
School-room at the mill, 36, 57.
Scott, Robert, bookseller, printing at Oxford by, 18.
Sellers, John, paper-maker, 70.
Settling-ponds at the mill, 9.

Sheldonian Theatre, press in the, 1668–1713, use of Wolvercote paper at, 13, 14, 15, 19, 20.
Simcock, J., millwright, 6 n.
Sole, the, room at the mill called, 23.
Stacy, J. H., manager (later Controller) of the mill 1855–83, 47, 48.
Stationers, Dutch and English, paper made in France by, 15.
— in London, paper sold to the University Press by, 14, 22, 24, 27.
Steam-power, use of, at the mill, 6.
Stewart, a paper-maker in 1720, 21.
Stone, John, carter at the mill, photograph of, *facing* p. 55.
Stonebridge, the, the Toll Bridge at Wolvercote called, 61 n.
Sulphite paper made at the mill, 50.
Sundays, opinion that Bible-paper should not be made on, 53.
Sutton Courtenay, Berks., paper-mill at, 70.
Swann (Swan), C. J., tenant of the mill *c.* 1817–22, 28.
— (Elizabeth), widow of John, mill managed by, 28.
— James, paper-maker at Eynsham, 25, 27, 28, 29.
— — occupier of the mill in 1816 and 1823, 29, 30, 62, 70.
— — Sandford Mill bought by, 29.
— John, lessee of the mill 1793–1806, 25–28.
— — watermarks attributed to, 25, 26.
— John the younger, occupier of the mill in 1842–4, 29, 63.
— William, paper-maker at Eynsham, 29.
Swann & Blake, paper-makers at Eynsham, 29.
Swann Brothers, firm of, bankruptcy of, in 1848, 29.
— — paper supplied to the University Press by, 25, 27, 29.
Sword-blades, proposed mill at Wolvercote for grinding, in 1643, 13.

Tarred paper made at Eynsham, 26.
Thames, navigation of the, 4, 62, 63.

Thames, upper, paper-mills on or near, 7, 70.
— volume of the, at Wolvercote, 1, 3.
— water of the, at Wolvercote, chemical analysis of, 1 n.
Thames Conservancy, 6, 9, 62, 63.
Thames Navigation Act, 1865, 4.
— Valley Drainage Board, acquisition of King's Weir by, 6.
'Tined', meadows said to be, 60.
Tithes of the mill and meadows in 1239, 11, 12.
Toll Bridge, the, at Wolvercote, 33, 61, 64.
Trade unions, 55, 56.

University of Oxford, acquisition of the mill by, 38. *See* Oxford.
— drawback of paper-duty allowed to, 71, 72.
University Press, Oxford. *See* Oxford, University Press at.
— Cambridge. *See* Cambridge.

Venables, Charles, paper-maker, 50, 70.
Vinerian Fellowship, candidate for, 27 n.

Wakefield, Robert, lessee of the mill 1773–82, 23, 67.
Walter, Sir John, of Sarsden, landlord of the mill, 13.
Watermarks, attributable to lessees of the mill, 16 n., 19, 25, 26.
— reasons for avoidance of, *c.* 1690, 16 n.
— statutory provision as to, 1794–1811, 72.
Water meadows by the mill, 27, 63, 64.
Water-power, former use of, by the mill, 1, 6, 7, 26, 54.
Water-rights of the mill, defended in 1865, 6.
Water-transport of coal, 7.
Water-wheels of the mill, 1, 23.
Webb's Close, Wolvercote, 64.
Weighbridge House, the, 27, 59.
Weir. *See* King's Weir.

Weirs Mill, Oxford, 8, 70.
Weller, family of, in Wolvercote, 10, 13, 63.
White Paper Makers, Company of, 16, 17, 66.
Williams, Mr., of Wolvercote, prosecution by, 62.
Wood, Anthony, quoted, 61.
Wood, paper made from, when first used at Oxford, 51, 53.
Wood-pulp, paper made from, at the mill, 9, 51, 53.

Worcester College, part of the mill-site bought from, 38, 59.
Wove paper, moulds for, bought by the Bible Press in 1787, 24.
— stocked by the University Press in 1798, 27.
Wright, Gill & Co., stationers, 24.

Yarnton, Duke's Lock in, 4.
— floods at, 3.
Yate, Thomas, Principal of Brasenose College, 14.

PRINTED IN GREAT BRITAIN
AT THE UNIVERSITY PRESS, OXFORD
BY CHARLES BATEY
PRINTER TO THE UNIVERSITY